DON'T SAY YOU CAN'T

A Personal Guide to Reading the Bible

Pastor Glenn—
Thank you for your friendship.
May God bless your ministry greatly!
Pastor Galen
SEP 2011

K. GALEN GREENWALT

ISBN 978-1-61364-305-1

Published by

Vision Plus Recovery Publishers

Rialto, California

For ordering, contact: revgalen@aol.com

Dewey Decimal Classification 207.0
Subject Heading: Bible, Study of
Library of Congress Card Catalog Number: 2011929592

Unless otherwise stated, all Scripture references used are from the King James Version (KJV).

Greenwalt, K. Galen, 1950 –

Don't Say You Can't *A Personal Guide to Reading the Bible* / K. Galen Greenwalt

ISBN 978-1-61364-305-1

AUTHOR'S DEDICATION

*Some years ago, this study was inspired by a couple of women
at The Vision Plus Church in Riverside,
a small Baptist church in Southern California.*

They simply asked for a basic knowledge of God's Word.

*I knew there were scores of books in the bookstores that could help them,
but I felt compelled to design a simple yet thorough walk through the Scriptures.*

The following pages are the result of that prompting.

Debi Shelton and Brenda Davis, this is for you.

Acknowledgements

As I complete this book, my family and friends need to be acknowledged.

My wife, Sondra, has always been a constant encouragement to me for all our years of marriage. Even when I have failed and faltered in different ways, she has been my defender and comfort and solid rock. We have had some amazing times together, and I am grateful to be married for nearly 40 years to one who loves me so dearly and to the one I love so dearly as well.

My three kids – Jason, Evan and Crystal – all have brought me great joy in life. I am proud of each of them in so many ways. They have shown me love and affection, and I feel honored to be their dad. They have been an inspiration to me as they have matured into adulthood.

My dad, Rev. A. L. Greenwalt, was my role model for ministry, even when I didn't know I would be serving in the pastorate for my calling in life.

My mom, Alice Bergeron Greenwalt, was (and still is) a wonderful mother who gives of herself freely and gladly for her children. She gave me training, guidance and discipline with great love.

My five brothers (Truett, David, Noel, John and Roger) and one sister (Marti) have been great fun as siblings and now have become great friends as we grow older.

In addition, I must name a few friends through the years who have been my source of encouragement in good times and not-so-good times. Don and Judy Nason are pillars of strength for me. Doris Robinson has been a second "mom" to me and Sondra, and she is so special. Randy and Vicki Smith are ones that are near and dear to me. Lorn and Sharon Harrison are always there when needed.

As a special tribute, I must acknowledge my best friend – a friend from college days to seminary study sessions to church life to various ministry pursuits to special family times – James Leroy Murcray. Pastor Jim Murcray pushed me and allowed me to be a partner in various ministry pursuits for many years until God called him home in 2009. We love his wife, Patricia, dearly too.

My church family for the last 10 years in *The Vision Plus Church* in Riverside has been wonderful to me as I share my heart in the church setting. This is an unusual church in many ways, and that is a good thing. Thanks go to the many who are involved deeply in the ministry of the congregation – Roy and Mary Flint, Jim Lunak, Jack Shelton, Cindy Guerin, "Big Jim" Ward, Wayne and Lynn Peters. This list also includes Pastor George Nelson and Pastor Michael Dotson, church starters in Chatsworth and Bakersfield respectively, as well as Pastor Ed McDowell serving in missions in the Philippines.

I want to say a special word about my friends in the Good News *Sober Living Program* at the Coronado Stone manufacturing plant in Fontana. Mr. Mel Bacon, owner of the company, has allowed me to do ministry work with newly-released parolees. I am thankful for the opportunity to learn and grow from these men who have shown me what it means to be open and transparent and authentic.

Lastly, I want to thank a good friend, Michael Geiger, who designed the book cover and helped in so many other ways with the printing format of this book.

Study
To show thyself approved
Unto God,
A workman that needeth not
To be ashamed,
Rightly dividing
The Word of Truth.

2 Timothy 2:15 (KJV)

TABLE OF CONTENTS

FOREWORD

Have you read the Bible from cover to cover? Have you read your Bible all the way through?

Over the years, I have asked this question to many people. Sadly, most have not read God's Word in its entirety. In fact, in my imperfect calculations, I have found that about 10% of Christians have read the entire Bible.

That is a testament to the shallowness of our church in today's society. In times past, we as Christians were called the "people of the Book." That meant we knew what Scripture had to say and we did our best to abide by it.

Now, when many Christians do not know what the Bible says, they have a hard time defending their beliefs which have been passed down to them through church tradition and doctrinally-sound preaching and teaching. Believers find themselves "parroting" others. That will not stand the test of examination and challenges by those of other faiths.

In discussion about basic theology and Biblical doctrine, it is not enough to say, "Well, that's what I was told. That's what my preacher said, and he wouldn't lie!" It's not enough to just repeat the thoughts and beliefs of others. We must be intimately acquainted with the verses of the Bible that speak to our morals and ethics and values and actions and beliefs and faith.

Otherwise, we are sitting ducks, waiting to be shot down as we try to defend our beliefs. We cannot convince others by saying, "Well, that's just the way it is. It believe it, and that's enough for me." Yes, that may be enough for you, but God calls us to draw others into the family of believers by both our faith and knowledge.

This is my challenge to you, the reader. Don't let anything stop you from reading God's personal revelation of Himself through Scripture.

Make a commitment deep within: "Yes, I will stay the course of reading the Bible through."

You will be blessed beyond your wildest dreams!

PREFACE

The study of the Bible can be done with any and all translations. There are so many that are helpful and more easily read than others.

The reader is asked to find a translation that helps with understanding and clarity, while staying true to the original texts of Hebrew, Aramaic and Greek.

The author has used the Authorized King James Version (1611) in preparation of the questions and answers. The KJV may be difficult for some, but it still has a magnificent way of bringing both prose and poetry to life as it reveals God's message of redemption and hope for the ages.

AUTHOR'S INTRODUCTION

As we read in Scripture, the church is the bride of Christ. In essence, the church is therefore the "wife," the bride, of a holy God.

So, I use the acrostic *WIFE* to illustrate the point of how the church is to function and serve the Lord. Using the letters *W * I * F * E*, the church is to…

W	=	Worship
I	=	Instruct
F	=	Fellowship
E	=	Evangelize

W = WORSHIP: The church is to worship, to bring both individuals and the corporate body to the point of communion in and celebration of God's presence.

I = INSTRUCT: The church is to instruct, to assist those who have a desire to study God's Word and find a deeper understanding through knowledge of the Bible.

F = FELLOWSHIP: The church is to fellowship, to bridge man-made barriers in order to bring unity and deeper intimacy of relationship with fellow believers.

E = EVANGELIZE: The church is to evangelize, to proclaim the Good News of redemption for all mankind through the atoning death, burial and resurrection of the Lord Jesus Christ, the very Son of God.

This is a study designed to help the church do its part of instruction.

There are other ways to accomplish this. It can be done through the Sunday School program, home Bible studies throughout the week, through correspondence and internet studies, or by a host of other means. This study, though, is prepared for those who may wish to do a personal and individual approach. It certainly can be used in the group setting, but that is not necessary.

I make no claim to be a theologian or research specialist. I am simply a pastor who wants to "feed sheep," that is, to assist fellow believers and church members to learn and grow in Christ though study of the Word. I trust that whoever uses this study might be fed from the bounty of Heaven's abundance. Truly, what one puts into this study is what one will get out of it. May each reader and student put much into the study of Scripture. It is necessary, powerful and rewarding!

I must make one last point, and this is critically important.

This is designed to help a reader dig out facts and information and details and knowledge. It is like digging for nuggets of precious stone. When you find these nuggets, you will figure out what to do next.

Therefore, this is a study of *what the Bible says* and so it not a commentary on *what it means*.

There is a great difference between the two. I have my own biases, my own interpretations, my own theology and my own thoughts on how Scripture should be interpreted and implemented. I will not do that here, however.

The most important thing is for one to know Scripture and then to allow the Spirit of God to teach and bring understanding. Yes, I will assist my congregation and others to know what Scripture means and how to live life, but some of you reading this are not part of my ministry covering. You have others that you will ask to help you know what the Bible means after you know what it says. That is wonderful!

Because of that, I will not attempt to teach meaning. That is for you to find through other means – your pastor, your Bible study leader, a commentary, personal communion with God through the power of the Holy Spirit, and so many other ways.

Therefore, I do encourage you and ask you to find someone to discuss the Bible knowledge you gain through this study. It will cement the truths that God has for you!

Have fun and enjoy God's word for your life!

35 Week
Study Guide

This may be helpful for the reader to keep a focus and to set a "finish line" for study.

Week 1:	Genesis
Week 2:	Exodus
Week 3:	Leviticus, Numbers
Week 4:	Deuteronomy
Week 5:	Joshua
Week 6:	Judges, Ruth
Week 7:	1 and 2 Samuel
Week 8:	1 and 2 Kings
Week 9:	1 and 2 Chronicles
Week 10:	Ezra, Nehemiah, Esther
Week 11:	Job
Week 12:	Psalms
Week 13:	Proverbs, Ecclesiastes, Song of Solomon
Week 14:	Isaiah
Week 15:	Jeremiah
Week 16:	Lamentations, Ezekiel
Week 17:	Daniel

Week 18:	Hosea, Joel, Amos
Week 19:	Obadiah, Jonah
Week 20:	Micah, Nahum, Habakkuk
Week 21:	Zephaniah, Haggai, Zechariah, Malachi
Week 22:	Matthew
Week 23:	Mark
Week 24:	Luke
Week 25:	John
Week 26:	Acts
Week 27:	Romans
Week 28:	1 and 2 Corinthians
Week 29:	Galatians, Ephesians
Week 30:	Philippians, Colossians
Week 31:	1 and 2 Thessalonians
Week 32:	1 and 2 Timothy, Titus, Philemon
Week 33:	Hebrews, James
Week 34:	1 and 2 Peter, 1 and 2 and 3 John
Week 35:	Jude, Revelation

When completed, it will be exciting to say: "Congratulations, you did it!"

BEGINNING THE JOURNEY

Reading the Bible! Sounds easy enough.

People read books every day. Four hundred thousand books of the latest Harry Potter series were just released. Other top-selling books line the shelves of bookstores and major distributors of novels and non-fiction. We read something everyday. It may be a newspaper. It may be an article or an email on the internet. We read billboards, road signs and advertisements. Reading is part of our daily life.

Well, what about reading the Bible? Oh, that's a different story!

We have different reasons for not reading the Bible:

> "I can't understand it."

> "I don't have time to digest it and have it make sense."

> "I will read it in my leisure time."

> "I don't know where to start."

> "I am just too busy and it will still be there later."

> "I'm not sure it's really true."

> "I don't know if it will help me."

Right now, it doesn't matter what your reasons or excuses have been for not reading the Bible. Let's make a statement and stand by it: "The Bible is worth reading!"

For the person who believes that the Bible is true and relevant, that is no problem. For the person who is not sure about the significance or importance of the Bible, is may be true for philosophical or general reading purposes. To be honest, I don't care what purpose an individual has when reading the Bible. From a pastor's perspective, there is amazing purpose and eternal consequences when someone reads the Word of God.

With that in mind, I have written this guide to the Bible with a specific purpose. I want people to read God's Word and gain understanding. Along the way in my ministry, many have come to me and complained that they need to know the Bible better. They want to feel more confident, more learned and more secure in their understanding of Scripture. They feel inadequate to discuss doctrine or theology or church practice. They feel clueless in basic Bible stories and gospel narratives. They believe they lack the knowledge to help them in discussion, presentation or involvement for ministry work.

That is the purpose of this workbook.

However, I must first caution the reader at this point. Upon completion of this book, you will not be a noted scholar and have all wisdom. This book is simply the starting place, the springboard, for you to know what the Bible says.

There is a vast difference in knowing what the Bible says and knowing what the Bible means. Some people equate the two, thinking that if you know what the Bible says then you know what it means. Not true!

For example, the Bible says that God spoke everything into existence. What does that mean? Does it mean that he audibly shouted out intelligible words and subsequently some kind of earthly matter came into being? Or does it mean that he called all substance into being by his awesome and creative nature? Theologians and "regular church folk" alike have debated things like this over the centuries.

What I believe is important is this. One cannot know what the Bible means until one knows what the Bible says!

So, let's start with the basics.

What does the Bible say?

In the following pages, I have presented several segments for you, the reader, to look at.

DIVISIONS.
First, I have separated the Bible into ten divisions, simply to give chunks of reading that are fairly equal in size. There is no spiritual or divine reason for these divisions, other than giving fair space and time for reading and learning. I have given a short summary to describe each division for the reader to be aware of.

SECTIONS.
Second, I have divided the divisions into several sections. These sections will be comprised of one or more books of the Bible. Some sections may even be a part of a book (the book of Matthew, for example). The reason for this is because some books are very short, some are very lengthy and the others are of moderate reading volume.

PASSAGES AND THEMES.
Third, the sections have been broken down into lengths of passages (chapters and verses) and themes contained therein. Again, the passages are divided into topical themes. This gives the reader some insight into what is about to be presented, read and studied. Hopefully, there will be a sense of fascination and intrigue about the next topic of study.

VERSES TO REMEMBER.

Fourth, the verses that have been chosen have held special significance over the centuries for believers. They give encouragement, challenge, doctrine and invitation to respond. Because the Bible is God's divine and personal word to mankind, it does everything a conversation can do. It demands a response. Please read the "Verses to Remember" with a heart to hear God speaking. Take time to respond to his voice.

A great preacher and pastor, Dr. W. A. Criswell, once wrote a book about the "Scarlet Thread through the Bible." His intention was to show the thread of God's redemptive purpose through the whole of Scripture. The scarlet thread was the blood sacrifice and atonement for sin. This saving sacrifice of Jesus brought about forgiveness, which all of mankind needs because "all have sinned and come short of the glory of God." Dr. Criswell talked about God's redemptive nature as seen in the Bible from Genesis all the way through to the final book of Revelation. The repentance and faith on the individual's part, combined with forgiveness and redemption on God's part, is a very personal and individual experience. As you read the Bible, let me ask you to look for the redemptive thread. Know what the Bible says, but also know what it says to you!

Now, this workbook consists of Questions and Answers. The answers needed may be True/False, Fill-In or Multiple Choice. Sorry, no essay questions here! Seriously, these questions are posed to give you a chance to read, study and write. It has been shown that greater retention of knowledge occurs when a person uses various methods to gain information.

Read all the questions for each Section first before studying the passages. You may even want to put pre-test answers down to measure how much you knew (or didn't know) prior to going through the passages. I want you to be ready to see what lies ahead in your journey through the Scriptures, so do take time to review all the questions first.

Next, read the passages. You may want to write the answers in the workbook as soon as you find an answer. However, I suggest that you wait until you have finished the whole passage in its entirety. This will force you to go back and seek the answers later. This review will help cement the knowledge in your mind. The more you see it and say it and write it, the deeper it will go into your memory bank. This brings a greater confidence and self-assurance about what the Bible says.

Lastly, I will ask you to summarize each book of the Bible in your own words. This is not an assessment or examination that God will look at and grade you! It is just a way for you to bring together what you have learned from that particular book. Don't look at commentaries or ask someone else what they think. Put down what you have learned. It's personal to you and you alone! You will be amazed as you see what you have gained by personal study.

Have a great journey through the Bible! And, remember, when reading the Bible through…..

Don't Say You Can't !!

THE BOOKS OF THE BIBLE

OLD TESTAMENT

Genesis
Exodus
Leviticus
Numbers
Joshua
Judges
Ruth
1 Samuel
2 Samuel
1 Kings
2 Kings
1 Chronicles
2 Chronicles
Ezra
Nehemiah
Esther
Job
Psalms
Proverbs
Ecclesiastes
Song of Solomon
Isaiah
Jeremiah
Lamentations
Ezekiel
Daniel
Hosea
Joel
Amos
Obadiah
Jonah
Micah
Nahum
Habakkuk
Zephaniah
Haggai
Zechariah
Malachi

NEW TESTAMENT

Matthew
Mark
Luke
Acts
Romans
1 Corinthians
2 Corinthians
Galatians
Ephesians
Philippians
Colossians
1 Thessalonians
2 Thessalonians
1 Timothy
2 Timothy
Titus
Philemon
Hebrews
James
1 Peter
2 Peter
1 John
2 John
3 John
Jude
Revelation

39 Old Testament books

27 New Testament books

(66 books total)

BRIEF OVERVIEW OF THE BIBLE

OLD TESTAMENT

Division 1:	Genesis – Deuteronomy	Beginnings, Patriarchs, Slavery and Wanderings
Division 2:	Joshua – 2 Chronicles	Promised Land, Judges and Kings, Israel Divided
Division 3:	Ezra – Ezekiel	Exile, Writings of David and Solomon, Major Prophets
Division 4:	Daniel - Malachi	Daniel and Minor Prophets

NEW TESTAMENT

Division 5:	Matthew – Mark	Jesus as Messiah and Savior
Division 6:	Luke – John	Jesus the Christ and His Teachings
Division 7:	Acts – Romans	Early Church and Doctrine
Division 8:	1 Corinthians – Colossians	Letters of Challenge and Encouragement
Division 9:	1 Thessalonians – Philemon	Instructions and Theology for the Church
Division 10:	Hebrews – Revelation	Right Living and Last Things

Section 1 - GENESIS

GENESIS

PASSAGE	_THEME_
Genesis 1:1 – 2:7	Creation Account
Genesis 2:8 – 3:24	Sin and the Fall of man
Genesis 6:1 – 9:19	Noah and the Flood
Genesis 11:1-9	Confusion of Languages
Genesis 12:1 – 22:19	Abraham
Genesis 21:1 – 27:46	Isaac
Genesis 25:19 – 35:29	Jacob / Israel
Genesis 29:32 – 30:24, 35:16	Jacob's 12 sons
Genesis 37:1 – 48:22	Joseph
Genesis 49:1-27	Blessings on the 12 Tribes of Israel

VERSES TO REMEMBER: _Genesis 1:1_   _God and Creation_
Genesis 12:2   _The Covenant with Abraham_

Section 1 – REVIEW of GENESIS

GENESIS

1. What did God create on each day in the creation account?

   Day 1:_____

   Day 2:_____

   Day 3:_____

   Day 4:_____

   Day 5:_____

   Day 6:_____

2. In the Garden of Eden, two trees are named. What are they?

   (1) The tree of _____.

   (2) The tree of _____.

3. God told Adam and Eve that they must not eat of the fruit of the tree in the midst of the Garden.

       True   /or/   False

4. The serpent directly contradicted God's command by saying that they would not die if they ate the fruit.
              True   /or/   False

5. What were the names of the first two children born to Adam and Eve: _____ and _____

6. How old was Methuselah when he died?_____

7. What were the dimensions of the ark that Noah built?

   Length:_____

   Width:_____

   Height:_____

10

8. How old was Noah when the flood waters came?_____

9. What did God say was the token of his covenant with Noah?_____

10. God called Abram (later named Abraham) and told him exactly where he was sending him.

        True   /or/   False

11. Abraham had a son by his handmaid, Hagar. The child's name was:_____

12. Abraham had a son by his wife, Sarah, and the child's name was:_____

13. How old was Abraham when Isaac was born?_____

14. Who was chosen to be Isaac's wife?_____

15. Isaac and Rebekah had twin boys. What were their names?

        (1)_____

        (2)_____

16. Jacob was tricked by his father-in-law. Which daughter did Jacob marry first?_____

17. How many years total did Jacob work for his father-in-law to marry Rachel?_____

18. Name the 12 sons of Jacob in order of birth:

        (1)_____

        (2)_____

        (3)_____

        (4)_____

        (5)_____

        (6)_____

        (7)_____

        (8)_____

(9)_____

(10)_____

(11)_____

(12)_____

19. Which two sons did Rachel give birth to? _____ and _____

20. When was Jacob's name changed to Israel?

    A.   When Jacob married Leah
    B.   When Jacob reconciled with his brother Esau
    C.   When Jacob's son Joseph was born
    D.   When Jacob wrestled with God at Peniel

21. Joseph was sold by his brothers to a group of merchants from what tribe?_____

22. Joseph was taken to Egypt and later interpreted dreams for:

    A.   the butler
    B.   the baker
    C.   the candlestick maker
    D.   the Pharaoh

23. What were the names of Joseph's two sons?

    (1)_____

    (2)_____

GENESIS. Write the main facts, ideas and your personal thoughts on the book of Genesis:

_____

_____

_____

Section 2 - EXODUS

EXODUS

PASSAGE   _THEME_

Exodus 2:1 – 4:18   Moses' Birth, Escape and Call
Exodus 4:19 – 15:21   Pharaoh, Passover and Exodus
Exodus 15:22 – 24:18   Wilderness and Feasts
Exodus 25:1 – 40:38   Ark and the Tabernacle

       VERSES TO REMEMBER: _Exodus 3:35_   _Standing on holy ground_
                                         Exodus 12:14   _Institution of Passover_
                                         Exodus 19:5   _God's Promise to His people_

Section 2 – REVIEW of EXODUS

EXODUS

1. Moses' father was from which tribe of Israel?_____

2. Who was paid by Pharaoh's daughter to nurse Moses?_____

3. The name "Moses" was given to him by:_____

4. What offense did Moses commit before running from Egypt?_____

5. Who appeared to Moses in the midst of a fiery burning bush?_____

6. What was Moses' first reaction to God's call to lead the Israelites out of Egypt?
    A. Excited, happy and positive
    B. Questioning, negative and pessimistic
    C. Sad, depressed and cautious

7. Because of Moses' excuses, God appointed _____ to be Moses' spokesman to the people.

8. Name the ten plagues that Moses commanded because of Pharaoh's unbelief:

    (1)_____

    (2)_____

    (3)_____

    (4)_____

    (5)_____

    (6)_____

    (7)_____

    (8)_____

    (9)_____

    (10)_____

9. For the death angel to pass over their houses, the Israelites were to smear _____ on the two side posts and on the upper door post of the house.

10. God led the Israelites in the wilderness with:

   (1) a pillar of _____ by day, and

   (2) a pillar of _____ by night.

11. What did Moses do to divide the Red Sea for the Israelites to cross over?

   a. Commanded the waters with words
   b. Stuck a rock with a rod
   c. Stretched out his hand over the waters

12. What two items did the Israelites eat every day during the 40 years of wandering in the wilderness?

   (1)_____

   (2)_____

13. Write out the Ten Commandments in your own words:

   (1)_____

   (2)_____

   (3)_____

   (4)_____

   (5)_____

   (6)_____

   (7)_____

   (8)_____

   (9)_____

   (10)_____

14. What were the dimensions of the ark of the testimony:

    (1) Length:_____

    (2) Width:_____

    (3) Height:_____

15. Aaron was commanded to make an atonement sacrifice upon the horns of the altar in the tabernacle with the blood of the sin offerings. How often was he to do this?

    a.   Once a year
    b.   Whenever there was sin in the camp
    c.   Every Sabbath

16. Which of the following is NOT true concerning the Sabbath?

    a.   The Sabbath is a sign between God and his people, showing that the Lord sanctifies them.
    b.   The Sabbath is to be kept holy.
    c.   The Sabbath is a day of rest.
    d.   The Sabbath is to be observed as a sign of obedience during the wilderness wanderings only.

17. Why did the Israelites ask Aaron to make a golden calf?

    a.   Because the Israelites had too much gold and didn't want to carry it any longer
    b.   Because the Israelites felt Moses was not coming back from the mount
    c.   Because the Israelites had always worshipped cows

EXODUS. Write the main facts, ideas and your personal thoughts on the book of Exodus:

_____

_____

_____

Section 3 – LEVITICUS, NUMBERS and DEUTERONOMY

LEVITICUS

PASSAGE

THEME

Leviticus 1:1 – 7:38   Regulations for Offerings and Sacrifices
Leviticus 16:1-34   Day of Atonement
Leviticus 23:1-44   Appointed Feasts
Leviticus 26:3-13   Blessings of Obedience
Leviticus 26:14-39   Discipline for Disobedience
Leviticus 26:40-46   Process of Reconciliation

VERSES TO REMEMBER: _Leviticus 17:11_   _The life is in the blood_
                         Leviticus 19:2   _The call to holiness_

NUMBERS

PASSAGE

THEME

Numbers 6:1-21   Nazarite Consecration Instructions
Numbers 13:1 – 14:45   Report of the 12 spies sent to Canaan
Numbers 22:1 – 24:25   Balaam and the Talking Donkey

VERSES TO REMEMBER: _Numbers 27:16-17_   _Pastors as shepherds_
                         Numbers 30:2   _Commitment_
                         Numbers 32:23   _Sin will be exposed_

DEUTERONOMY

PASSAGE

THEME

Deuteronomy 3:26-29   View of the Promised Land
Deuteronomy 4:1 – 5:21   Call to obedience
Deuteronomy 6:1-9   The Great Commandment
Deuteronomy 11:26-28   The Great Choice – Blessing or Curse
Deuteronomy 26:15-19   The Call to Covenant

VERSES TO REMEMBER: _Deuteronomy 1:12_   _Call to possess the land_
                         Deuteronomy 6:4   _One God_
                         Deuteronomy 10:12-13 _Requirements for Godly Living_
                         Deuteronomy 31:6   _Godly Courage_

Section 3 – REVIEW of LEVITICUS, NUMBERS and DEUTERONOMY

LEVITICUS

1. For the sin offering, the priest was instructed to dip his finger in the bullock's blood and sprinkle the blood _____ times before the veil of the sanctuary.

   A. three
   B. seven
   C. ten
   D. thirty

2. God destroyed two sons of Aaron for their sin of unholy incense. What were their names?

   (1)_____

   (2)_____

3. On the Day of Atonement, two goats were to be brought to Aaron. They would cast lots upon the two goats, one lot for the Lord and one lot for the _____.

   A. Scapegoat
   B. Priests
   C. Gentiles

4. After confessing the sins and transgressions over the head of the scapegoat, the priest would send the goat away by the hand of a fit man into the wilderness.

   True   /or/   False

5. According to the law of Moses, a man who committed adultery with another man's wife was to be:

   A. sent away from the community forever
   B. put to death
   C. made to pay a double sin offering

6. How often was the Year of Jubilee to be observed?_____

7. The tithe offering is to be given from the fruit or seed of the land, of the herd or the flock, and is:

   A. a tenth, belonging to the Lord and holy unto the Lord
   B. something that is voluntary according to the law of Moses
   C. not commanded by the law of Moses

18

NUMBERS

1. The numbering of the males was commanded with two factors recognized:

    (1) They were to be of what age?_____

    (2) They were to be able to go forth to do _____ in Israel.

2. What tribe was not numbered with the other tribes of Israel?

    A. Judah
    B. Benjamin
    C. Levi

3. Which of the following is NOT a law for the Nazarite vow?

    A. He shall not drink wine or other strong drink
    B. He shall eat nothing from the vine tree
    C. He shall shave his head clean of all hair
    D. He shall not touch a dead body

4. The Passover shall be observed on what month and day?

    A. Fourteenth day of the second month
    B. First day of the first month
    C. Last day of the first month

5. Twelve spies were sent into Canaan to assess the land and people. Two returned with a report of confidence in the Lord's ability to give them the land. Who were they?

    (1)_____

    (2)_____

6. How did God deal with the rebellion of Korah and his followers?

    A. An earthquake swallowed them up
    B. A fiery dragon ate them alive
    C. A swarm of serpents bit them and they died

7. Moses sinned when he struck the rock twice in Meribah to bring forth water.

    True /or/ False

8. Who was riding the donkey when the donkey spoke out loud?_____

9. Who was appointed to succeed Moses to lead the Israelites?_____

DEUTERONOMY

1. The Great Commandment says to love the Lord with all your:

      (1)_____

      (2)_____

      (3)_____

2. God's people are commanded to be:

      A. strong and of a good courage
      B. afraid and troubled
      C. naïve and careless

3. God said that he will never fail nor forsake his people.

      True   /or/   False

4. Moses was able to see and enter into the Promised Land before he died.

      True   /or/   False

LEVITICUS, NUMBERS, DEUTERONOMY. Write the main facts, ideas and your personal thoughts on the following books:

LEVITICUS:_____

NUMBERS:_____

_____

DEUTERONOMY:_____

_____

DIVISION TWO
JOSHUA - 2 CHRONICLES

Section 4 – JOSHUA, JUDGES and RUTH

JOSHUA

PASSAGE	*THEME*
Joshua 2:1 – 6:27	Fall of Jericho
Joshua 13:7 – 19:51	Taking of the Promised Land
Joshua 24:1-28	Joshua's Farewell Address

VERSES TO REMEMBER:

Joshua 1:9	*Boldness because God is near*
Joshua 24:15	*Choose you this day your God*

JUDGES

PASSAGE	*THEME*
Judges 1:21 – 3:7	Israel's Decline
Judges 6:11 – 8:32	Gideon
Judges 13:1 – 16:31	Samson

VERSES TO REMEMBER:

Judges 2:19	*The Lost Generation*
Judges 6:17	*Asking for a Sign*

RUTH

PASSAGE	*THEME*
Ruth 1:8 – 4:17	Lineage of King David

VERSE TO REMEMBER:

Ruth 1:16	*Pledge of Devotion*

Section 4 – REVIEW of JOSHUA, JUDGES and RUTH

JOSHUA

1. What was the name of the harlot who assisted the spies that were sent into Jericho?

   _____

2. The people of Israel were to stay how far apart from the priests and the ark when crossing the Jordan?

   D. 2,000 cubits
   E. 70 paces
   F. 200 feet

3. What weapons did the Israelites use to defeat the city of Jericho?

   A. Daggers and knives
   B. Swords and clubs
   C. Trumpets made of ram's horns

4. Achan sinned by keeping some of the treasure of Jericho. What was his punishment?

   A. Death by stoning
   B. Death by hanging
   C. Death by starvation

5. There is a list of kings defeated by Moses. How many kings were defeated by Joshua?

   A. None
   B. Seven
   C. Thirty-one

6. In Joshua's farewell address, he charged the Israelites to choose between the God of their fathers and:

   A. the gods of the Amorites
   B. the gods of the Euphrates
   C. the gods of the Nile

JUDGES

1. An angel of the Lord came up from Gilgal to Bochim and said, "I will _____ break my covenant with you."

    A. sometimes
    B. always
    C. never

2. The first Judge and Deliverer of the Israelites was Othniel, the son of Kenaz, Caleb's younger brother.

                True   /or/   False

3. Who drove a nail through the head of a man who was sleeping?_____

4. Gideon asked confirmation of the Lord's call when he asked for a sign. What kind of cloth was used?

    A. Hide of a cow
    B. Skin of a snake
    C. Fleece of wool

5. Gideon's army was reduced from 32,000 men down to _____.

6. The men in Gideon's army were instructed to hold:

        a lamp within a pitcher in their _____ hand, and
        a trumpet in their _____ hand.

7. The angel of the Lord commanded the parents of Samson, prior to his birth, to raise him in the tradition and vows of the _____.

    A. Nazarenes
    B. Nazaroons
    C. Nazarites

8. The tribes of Israel fought against the children of Benjamin at Gibeah.

    In the first battle, how many Israelites were killed?_____

    In the second battle, how many Israelites were killed?_____

    In the third and final battle, how many Benjamites were killed?_____

RUTH

1. Naomi had two daughters-in-law. What were their names?

     (1)_____

     (2)_____

2. Naomi was from what city?_____

3. Which daughter-in-law stayed with Naomi and later married Boaz?_____

4. Ruth's son, Obed, was the _____ of a boy who one day would be King David.

    A. father
    B. grandfather
    C. brother

JOSHUA, JUDGES, RUTH. Write the main facts, ideas and your personal thoughts on the following books:

JOSHUA:_____

_____

_____

JUDGES:_____

_____

_____

RUTH:_____

_____

_____

Section 5 – 1 SAMUEL and 2 SAMUEL

1 SAMUEL

PASSAGE   ### THEME

1 Samuel 1:1 – 3:21   Birth and Call of Samuel
1 Samuel 8:4 – 10:24   Saul chosen as first King of Israel
1 Samuel 16:1 – 17:58   David and Goliath
1 Samuel 19:8 – 26:25   Saul's jealousy of David

VERSES TO REMEMBER:		
	1 Samuel 12:22	*God will never forsake his own*
	1 Samuel 15:22	*Obedience is better than sacrifice*
	1 Samuel 16:7	*God looks on the heart*

2 SAMUEL

PASSAGE   ### THEME

2 Samuel 2:1 – 5:12   David crowned as next King
2 Samuel 6:1 – 7:29   The Call to build the Temple
2 Samuel 11:1 – 12:25   David's Sin and Repentance
2 Samuel 21:1 – 24:25   David's return to Jerusalem and Last Days

VERSES TO REMEMBER:		
	2 Samuel 7:13	*Establishing God's Kingdom*
	2 Samuel 7:26	*Magnifying the Name of the Lord*

Section 5 – REVIEW of 1 SAMUEL and 2 SAMUEL

1 SAMUEL

1. Hannah prayed that she might bear a child. The priest Eli thought:

    A. Hannah was lost from her family.
    B. Hannah was drunk.
    C. Hannah was looking for a shopping center.

2. After Samuel was weaned, he was brought to the temple to live with the priest Eli and his family.

    True   /or/   False

3. After Samuel was born, Hannah had more children:

    A. Three sons and two daughters
    B. Two sons and three daughters
    C. Five sons and five daughters

4. God called Samuel three times during the night. Eli told Samuel to respond to God by saying:

    A. "O God, I am the righteous one."
    B. "Lord, is it you?"
    C. "Speak, Lord, for your servant is listening."

5. Samuel confronted the nation of Israel about their sin in Mizpeh. After repenting they went to battle and defeated the Philistines. Samuel took a stone and set it between Mizpeh and Shen and called it:

    _____

6. In Samuel's day, God used judges to lead and rule the people of Israel. However, when Samuel became old the elders gathered in Ramah and demanded that they have a:

    A. party.
    B. land grant ceremony.
    C. king.

7. The first king of Israel was anointed by Samuel and installed as king at _____.

8. Saul and his army defeated the Amalekites but, in disobedience, spared King Agag.

    True   /or/   False

9. Samuel was instructed by God to find another king to succeed Saul. Where was Samuel sent?

    A. Mizpeh
    B. Bethlehem
    C. Jerusalem

10. The son of Jesse named _____ was anointed to be the next king.

11. David defeated Goliath in a one-on-one battle. In today's measurement, how tall was Goliath?

    A. 9 feet 9 inches
    B. 6 feet 6 inches
    C. 3 feet 3 inches

12. David married which daughter of King Saul?_____

13. King Saul became jealous of David's popularity and:

    A. threw a party.
    B. plotted to kill David.
    C. sent his daughter away.

14. David's best friend with whom he made a covenant was named:_____.

15. David had several chances to kill King Saul but spared his life.

    True   /or/   False

2 SAMUEL

1. After defeating Saul's sons, David was made king of both Judah and Israel at

_____.

2. How many years total did King David reign, combining his reign in Judah and Israel?_____

3. David extended kindness of Jonathan's son, whose feet were crippled. What was the son's name?

    A. Mephibosheth
    B. Saul III
    C. Jonathan Jr.

4. David committed adultery with Bathsheba, and a son was born. What was this son's name?

    A. Mephibosheth
    B. Nathan
    C. Solomon

5. The name of the prophet that rebuked King David about sin was _____.

6. David's son, _____, rebelled against his father and was killed by Joab.

1 SAMUEL, 2 SAMUEL. Write the main facts, ideas and your personal thoughts on the following books:

1 SAMUEL:_____

_____

_____

2 SAMUEL:_____

_____

_____

Section 6 – 1 KINGS, 2 KINGS, 1 CHRONICLES and 2 CHRONICLES

1 KINGS

PASSAGE	*THEME*
1 Kings 1:28 – 2:12	Solomon made King upon David's death
1 Kings 3:3-28	Solomon's Prayer for Wisdom
1 Kings 5:1 – 8:66	The Building of the Temple
1 Kings 11:41 – 12:33	Solomon's Death and a Divided Israel
1 Kings 17:1 – 19:21	Ministry and Miracles of Elijah

VERSES TO REMEMBER:	*1 Kings 18:21*	*Choose Baal or God*
	1 Kings 19:12	*The still small voice of God*

2 KINGS

PASSAGE	*THEME*
2 Kings 2:1-11	Elijah's last days and ride to Heaven
2 Kings 2:12 – 8:15	Ministry and Miracles of Elisha
2 Kings 18:1 – 20:21	Reign of King Hezekiah
2 Kings 24:1 – 25:30	The Fall of Jerusalem

VERSES TO REMEMBER:	*2 Kings 2:9*	*Double portion of Spirit on Elisha*
	2 Kings 19:31	*The promise of the remnant of Israel*

1 CHRONICLES

PASSAGE	*THEME*
1 Chronicles 10:1-14	Death of King Saul by God's Hand
1 Chronicles 13:1 – 16:43	The Importance and Holiness of the Ark of the Covenant
1 Chronicles 21:1 – 22:19	King David's Purchase and Preparation of the Temple Site

VERSES TO REMEMBER:	*1 Chronicles 1:25*	*Shortest verse in the Old Testament*
	1 Chronicles 4:10	*The Prayer of Jabez*
	1 Chronicles 28:9	*Command to Know and Serve God*

2 CHRONICLES

PASSAGE

THEME

2 Chronicles 1:1 – 7:22	Solomon's Humility, Wealth, and Dedication
2 Chronicles 17:1 – 21:1	Religious reforms under King Jehoshaphat
2 Chronicles 29:1 – 32:33	King Hezekiah restores Temple worship

VERSES TO REMEMBER:

	2 Chronicles 6:18	*Nothing can contain fullness of God*
	2 Chronicles 7:14	*True Restoration through Repentance*
	2 Chronicles 15:3	*Formula for Spiritual Disaster*

Section 6 – REVIEW 1 KINGS, 2 KINGS, 1 CHRONICLES and 2 CHRONICLES

1 KINGS

1. David instructed Zadok, Nathan and Benaiah to anoint Solomon the next king in what city?

    A. Gihon
    B. Gilead
    C. Gebron

2. Solomon prayed for wisdom, and God granted him:

    A. a beautiful wife and many children.
    B. a multitude of chariots and a mighty army.
    C. wisdom, riches and long life.

3. The size of the Temple which God instructed Solomon to build was:

    A. 500 feet long, 500 feet wide and 500 feet high
    B. 90 feet long, 30 feet wide and 45 feet high
    C. 600 feet long, 200 feet wide and 300 feet high

4. After Solomon' death, there was division in the land. Two kings were anointed:

    _____ was made king over the land of Judah

    _____ was made king over the land of Israel

5. King Ahab married a woman named _____.

6. The prophet Elijah was told to go into hiding. He was fed by _____.

7. Elijah was unable to perform miracles or raise the dead.

    True /or/ False

8. A contest of gods was held on Mount Carmel between Elijah and the prophets of Baal. What was the miraculous outcome?

    A. Fire consumed Elijah's sacrifice, wood, stones, dust and water
    B. Fire consumed the prophets of Baal
    C. Fire consumed Jezebel and her children

9. Elijah fled from Jezebel to the Mount of _____.

10. Elijah found a man to cast his mantle over and then became his spiritual mentor. Who was that man?

    A. Elisha
    B. Ahab
    C. Naboth

2 KINGS

1. Elijah was taken up in a whirlwind into heaven by:

    A. Abraham, Isaac and Jacob
    B. a chariot of fire and horses of fire
    C. a band of 12 angels

2. Elisha, taking the mantle of Elijah, stood and parted the waters of the river _____.

3. Naaman had leprosy and was angry with Elisha, who told Namaan to:

    A. pray and fast for seven hours.
    B. bring sacrifices to the priests for seven days.
    C. dip seven times in the Jordan River.

4. King Jehu ordered Jezebel to be thrown from her tower to her death.

    True   /or/   False

5. Jerusalem fell captive to the King of Babylon named:

    A. Nebuchadnezzar
    B. Hezekiah
    C. Josiah

1 CHRONICLES

1. Jabez was a descendant of:

    A. Judah
    B. Nebuchadnezzar
    C. Sennacherib

2. The man who put his hand to the ark was struck down in death by God. His name was

_____.

3. The angel of God told Gad to instruct King David to set up an altar in the threshing floor of Ornan.

True   /or/   False

2 CHRONICLES

1. Solomon named the two pillars that were erected with the Temple. The names were:

   (1) On the right hand, _____.

   (2) On the left hand, _____.

2. After the ark was brought in, they praised God and the temple was filled with a _____.

3. After Solomon's prayer of dedication, the offerings and sacrifices were consumed by:

   a.   the priests and Levites.
   b.   strange animals from the forest.
   c.   fire from heaven.

4. For God to hear, forgive and heal in Israel's land, what did God tell Solomon the people must do?

   "If my people which are called by my name shall:

   (1) _____,

   (2) and _____,

   (3) and _____,

   (4) and _____,

   ...then will I hear from heaven, and will forgive their sin, and will heal their land."

5. King Ahaz was taken captive by the king of Syria. The Syrians killed _____ of the army of Judah in one day, because the people had forsaken the Lord God.

   A.   120
   B.   1,200
   C.   120,000

6. Hezekiah wrote to all Israel and Judah to bring a divided nation together to worship at the feast of:

_____

1 KINGS, 2 KINGS, 1 CHRONICLES, 2 CHRONICLES. Write the main facts, ideas and your personal thoughts on the following books:

1 KINGS:_____

_____

2 KINGS:_____

_____

1 CHRONICLES:_____

_____

2 CHRONICLES:_____

_____

DIVISION THREE
EZRA - EZEKIEL

Section 7 – EZRA, NEHEMIAH, ESTHER and JOB

EZRA

PASSAGE   *THEME*

Ezra 1:1-11   Israel's return from Exile in Babylon
Ezra 3:1-13   Restoration of Passionate Worship
Ezra 4:1 – 6:22   The Temple is rebuilt in Jerusalem

    VERSES TO REMEMBER: *Ezra 3:12-13*   *The Passionate Response in Worship*
                                            Ezra 10:1   *Revival and Confession*

NEHEMIAH

PASSAGE   *THEME*

Nehemiah 1:4-11   Nehemiah's Prayer for Jerusalem
Nehemiah 2:1 – 6:19   Nehemiah leads the Building of the Jerusalem Walls
Nehemiah 8:1 – 10:39   God's Word, Worship and Repentance

    VERSES TO REMEMBER: *Nehemiah 1:9*   *Formula for Spiritual Restoration*
                                            Nehemiah 4:6   *The Importance of Working Together*
                                            Nehemiah 9:17   *The Character of God*

ESTHER

PASSAGE   *THEME*

Esther 1:10 – 2:18   Esther crowned Queen of Persia
Esther 2:19 – 9:19   Plot to destroy all Jews and its end result
Esther 9:20 -32   Feast of Purim instituted

    VERSE TO REMEMBER: *Esther 4:14*   *An appointed time in history for Esther*

JOB

PASSAGE   *THEME*

Job 1:1 – 3:26   God allowed Job's suffering
Job 4:1 – 5:27   Job rebuked by friends for apparent sin
Job 9:1 – 10:22   Job acknowledges God's justice but still complains to God
Job 13:1-28   Job defends his integrity

Job 38:1 – 40:24   God's challenge brings humility
Job 42:1-17   Job's full submission to God and resulting blessings

VERSES TO REMEMBER: *Job 1:21-22*   *Refusal to Sin in the Face of Despair*
                        Job 19:25   *Job's Statement of Faith*

Section 7 – REVIEW of EZRA, NEHEMIAH, ESTHER and JOB

EZRA

1. The king of Persia felt compelled to rebuild the temple of Jerusalem. What was his name?_____

2. The foundation of the temple was laid, and the people of God:

    a. wept and shouted with joy.
    b. complained that it took so long.
    c. killed the chief builders.

3. After the rebuilding of the temple, which king made a decree which allowed anyone to return home?

    a. Cyrus
    b. Ezra
    c. Artaxerxes

NEHEMIAH

1. Nehemiah served King Artaxerxes in _____, the place of the palace.

2. The three main adversaries who ridiculed and opposed Nehemiah were:

    (1) _____, the Horonite

    (2) _____, the Ammonite and servant

    (3) _____, the Arabian.

3. Upon the rebuilding of the walls of Jerusalem, the people gathered to hear Ezra read from:

    A. the book of myths and legends.
    B. the book of records of tithes and offerings.
    C. the book of the law of Moses.

ESTHER

1. The name of the queen who refused to appear before King Ahasuerus was _____.

2. The fair young virgin chosen to replace Vashti was _____.

41

3. Haman devised a plot to kill Esther's cousin and guardian, _____, and all Jews.

4. Haman finally succeeded in getting Mordecai hanged on the gallows which were 75 feet high.

        True   /or/   False

5. The deliverance of the Jews from this massacre is celebrated during a feast called:

    A. Feast of Mordecai
    B. Feast of Esther
    C. Feast of Purim

JOB

1. God gave Satan permission to test Job.
                  True   /or/   False

2. In one day, the following occurred in the life of Job:

    (1) the _____ were taken and the servants killed by the Sabeans

    (2) a fire from heaven burned up the _____ and the servants,

    (3) the _____ were taken and the servants killed by the Chaldeans

    (4) the _____ of Job were killed when the house fell on them.

3. When Job became infected with boils from head to foot, his wife told him to:

    A. Trust God and live.
    B. Believe in the miraculous work of the prophets.
    C. Curse God and die.

4. Job's friends were a constant _____ to him.

        A. source of encouragement
        B. source of criticism
        C. source of finances

5. At the end of Job's testing, God rewarded him with _____ as much as before.

    A. not
    B. the same in amount
    C. twice

EZRA, NEHEMIAH, ESTHER, JOB. Write the main facts, ideas and your personal thoughts on the following books:

EZRA:_____

_____

NEHEMIAH:_____

_____

ESTHER:_____

_____

JOB:_____

_____

Section 8 – PSALMS, PROVERBS, ECCLESIASTES and SONG OF SOLOMON

PSALMS

PASSAGE	THEME
Psalm 1	The Righteous Man is Faithful and Blessed
Psalm 5	Prayer of Devotion and Confidence
Psalm 7	Prayer for Deliverance
Psalm 13	Prayer to Overcome Discouragement
Psalm 23	Awareness of God's Comfort
Psalm 37	Formula for Living the Godly Life
Psalm 51	Prayer for a Clean Heart
Psalm 90	The Importance of Time
Psalm 103	Formula for Thanksgiving to God
Psalm 136	Repetition of Praise for God's Mercy

VERSES TO REMEMBER:

Psalm 8:1	*The excellence of God's name*
Psalm 27:14	*Wait on the Lord*
Psalm 34:1	*Bless the Lord at all times*
Psalm 46:1	*God is our help in trouble*
Psalm 100:2	*Serve the Lord with gladness*
Psalm 119:105	*God's Word is our guide for life*
Psalm 143:10	*Prayer for God's Instruction*

PROVERBS

PASSAGE	THEME
Proverbs 1	The Way of Wisdom
Proverbs 3	Rewards of Wisdom
Proverbs 5	Warning against Immorality
Proverbs 6:16-19	Seven Things God Hates
Proverbs 14:1 – 16:33	Contrast Between Wisdom and Foolishness
Proverbs 22:1-6	What to Teach Your Children

VERSES TO REMEMBER:

Proverbs 1:7	*Fear of Lord is Beginning of Wisdom*
Proverbs 3:5-6	*Trust God for all your Ways*
Proverbs 15:1	*A Soft Answer Turns Away Anger*
Proverbs 17:17	*A true Friend*
Proverbs 29:18	*No Vision, People Perish*

ECCLESIASTES

PASSAGE   *THEME*

Ecclesiastes 1:1-18   The Pros and Cons of Wisdom
Ecclesiastes 4:9-12   Strength in Partnership
Ecclesiastes 5:1-7   Worship and Commitment
Ecclesiastes 7:1-8   The End is better than the Beginning
Ecclesiastes 8:6-17   Life is not always Fair

VERSES TO REMEMBER: *Ecclesiastes 7:20 No one is sinless*
                               Ecclesiastes 12:13-14   Summary of Life

SONG OF SOLOMON

PASSAGE   *THEME*

Song of Solomon 4:1-7   The Groom's Love for his Bride

VERSE TO REMEMBER: *Song of Solomon 2:4   His Banner over me is Love*

Section 8 – REVIEW of PSALMS, PROVERBS, ECCLESIASTES and SONG OF SOLOMON

PSALMS

1. In Psalm 1, the blessed man finds his delight in _____.

2. In Psalm 14, who says there is no God?_____

3. In Psalm 18:2, which of the following is NOT a description of God?

    A. my rock
    B. my high tower
    C. my shame

4. In Psalm 37:7, we are commanded to rest and wait _____ on the Lord.

5. According to Psalm 90:10, the average lifespan of man is _____ years.

6. How should we serve the Lord, according to Psalm 100:2?_____

7. In the six short verses of Psalm 150, how many times is the word "praise" used to call us to action?

    A. 6
    B. 10
    C. 13

PROVERBS

1. The fear and reverent awe of the Lord is the beginning of

    _____.

2. Where does wisdom come from, according to Proverbs 2:6?

    _____

3. To whom does the Lord give correction and discipline (Proverbs 3:12)?

    _____

4. In Proverbs 6:16-19, what are the seven things that are an abomination (things hated) to God?

47

(1)_____

(2)_____

(3)_____

(4)_____

(5)_____

(6)_____

(7)_____

5. What is one thing that will turn away anger and wrath, according to Proverbs 15:1?_____

6. In Proverbs 16:18, _____ precedes the fall and destruction of an individual.

7. Love, reputation and a good name are all better than _____.

8. In Proverbs 31, a woman that fears and worships God shall be _____.

ECCLESIASTES

1. According to the Preacher, everything in life (work, fun, wisdom, knowledge) comes to an end and is:

   A. emptiness and vanity
   B. worthwhile and eternal
   C. pleasurable and satisfying

2. When you vow a vow to God, be sure to _____.

3. In Ecclesiastes 12:13, what is the whole duty and purpose of man?

   (1)_____ and (2)_____

4. Who will judge every action, thought and word of our lives?_____

SONG OF SOLOMON

1. "This is my beloved and my _____" Song of Solomon 5:16

PSALMS, PROVERBS, ECCLESIASTES, SONG OF SOLOMON. Write the main facts, ideas and your personal thoughts on the following books:

PSALMS:_____

_____

PROVERBS:_____

_____

ECCLESIASTES:_____

_____

SONG OF SOLOMON:_____

_____

Section 9 - ISAIAH, JEREMIAH, LAMENTATIONS and EZEKIEL

ISAIAH

PASSAGE	THEME
Isaiah 1:10-31	Judah called to repent
Isaiah 6:1-11	Call and personal commitment of Isaiah
Isaiah 12:1-6	Praise to God
Isaiah 14:24 – 19:25	Prophetic warnings to major enemies of Judah
Isaiah 40:1-31	Words of Comfort
Isaiah 65:17 – 66:24	New Heaven

VERSES TO REMEMBER:

Isaiah 6:8	*Here am I, send me*
Isaiah 9:6-7	*Prophecy of Savior to come*
Isaiah 33:22	*God will save*
Isaiah 40:31	*Wait on the Lord*

JEREMIAH

PASSAGE	THEME
Jeremiah 1:4-19	Call of Jeremiah
Jeremiah 2:1-8	Message to sinful Israel
Jeremiah 4:1-8	Call to repentance and confession
Jeremiah 7:1-34	Pronouncement of impending judgment on Judah
Jeremiah 11:18 – 13:27	Jeremiah's personal life and lessons learned
Jeremiah 15:15-21	Jeremiah's complaint and God's assurance
Jeremiah 18:1-17	Lesson of the Potter
Jeremiah 20:1-18, 52:1-30	Jeremiah's Experiences in Prison
Jeremiah 28:1-17	Challenge of the False Prophet
Jeremiah 29:1 – 31:40	Promise of Restoration and a New Covenant
Jeremiah 37:1 – 38:13	Imprisonment and Rescue
Jeremiah 39:1-10	Fall of Jerusalem

VERSES TO REMEMBER:

Jeremiah 9:24	*Things the Lord delights in*
Jeremiah 17:7	*Blessed is the man who trusts in God*
Jeremiah 23:5	*A Righteous Branch will be raised up*
Jeremiah 30:22	*And you shall be my people*
Jeremiah 33:3	*Call unto God and he will answer*

LAMENTATIONS

<u>*PASSAGE*</u>   <u>*THEME*</u>

Lamentations 3   Even in Distress, There is Hope in the Lord
Lamentations 5   Prayer of Suffering

> *VERSE TO REMEMBER:*   *Lamentations 3:21-26*   *Therefore will I have hope in the Lord*

EZEKIEL

<u>*PASSAGE*</u>   <u>*THEME*</u>

Ezekiel 1:1 – 3:27   The Call of Ezekiel
Ezekiel 20:1 – 22:31   History of Rebellious Israel
Ezekiel 33:1-20   The Watchman's Duty and Call to Righteous Living
Ezekiel 37:1-28   The Valley of Dry Bones and the Restoration of Israel
Ezekiel 40:1 – 48:35   The Vision of the Temple

> *VERSES TO REMEMBER:*   *Ezekiel 11:19-20*   *New Spirit to live in obedience to God*
> *Ezekiel 18:4*   *The soul that sinneth, it shall die*
> *Ezekiel 44:28*   *God is our Inheritance*

Section 9 – REVIEW of ISAIAH, JEREMIAH, LAMENTATIONS and EZEKIEL

ISAIAH

1. The prophetic ministry of Isaiah was under the reign of four kings. Name them:

(1)_____

(2)_____

(3)_____

(4)_____

2. When the Lord asked whom he should send, Isaiah responded with, "Here am I, send...

   A. the king."
   B. the priest."
   C. me."

3. The Prince of Peace is prophesied by Isaiah. The prophetic word is found in:

   A. Isaiah 9:6-7
   B. Isaiah 6:8-9
   C. Isaiah 7:11-12

4. Isaiah chapter 18 is a prophecy concerning the nation of:

_____

5. Isaiah 33:22 reveals that the Lord is "our judge,...our lawgiver,...our _____..."

   A. king
   B. spokesman
   C. scapegoat

6. In Isaiah 61:1, Isaiah was anointed and called to preach good tidings to the meek, and also to:

(1)_____

(2)_____

(3)_____

JEREMIAH

1. When did God ordain Jeremiah to be a prophet among the nations?

    A. At age 31
    B. At age 13
    C. Before he was born

2. In Jeremiah 7:23, God says that he will be our God and we will be his people if we:

    A. Ignore his words
    B. Contradict his commands
    C. Obey his voice

3. Pashur, the son of Immer the priest, took Jeremiah and put him in:

    A. a royal house.
    B. the prison stocks.
    C. bright colored clothing.

4. The Lord poses a question to Jeremiah: "Is there anything too _____ for God?"

5. Jeremiah was rescued from the dungeon at the request to the king by Ebed-melech the:

    A. Egyptian
    B. Ethiopian
    C. Evolutionist

6. When Jerusalem fell, the king of _____ asked that no harm come to Jeremiah.

7. In Jeremiah chapter 52, the king of Babylon released _____, king of Judah, from prison and elevated him to sit on a throne above other kings that were with him in Babylon.

LAMENTATIONS

1. The writer of the Lamentations says that "the Lord is good...

    A. to those who wait for him and seek him."
    B. to those who are in deep distress."
    C. to those who are in Jerusalem."

EZEKIEL

1. Ezekiel was by the _____ river when the visions of God came to him.

2. Ezekiel was a _____, the son of Buzi in the land of the Chaldeans.

3. In Ezekiel 11:19-20, God says that he will restore his people by giving them:

    A. a new heart and a new spirit
    B. the land of their forefathers
    C. abundant wealth even in exile

4. According to Ezekiel 18:4, what will happen to the soul that sins?_____

5. What is the purpose of keeping the Sabbath holy? The Sabbaths are to be:

    A. a symbol of the war that exists between good and evil
    B. a signal of truce between God and man
    C. a sign between God and his people, that they might know God personally

6. God told Ezekiel to be a _____ for the house of Israel, and Ezekiel's responsibility was to warn Israel as he heard the word of the Lord directly given to him.

7. God commanded Ezekiel to preach to a:

    A. cave full of sleeping animals
    B. valley of dry bones
    C. lake full of dead fish

8. In Ezekiel's vision of the temple, how many days were needed to present sacrificial offerings to make atonement and purify the altar?

    A. 3
    B. 7
    C. 10

ISAIAH, JEREMIAH, LAMENTATIONS, EZEKIEL. Write the main facts, ideas and your personal thoughts on the following books:

ISAIAH:_____

_____

JEREMIAH:_____

_____

LAMENTATIONS:_____

_____

EZEKIEL:_____

_____

DIVISION FOUR
DANIEL - MALACHI

Section 10 – DANIEL, HOSEA, JOEL and AMOS

DANIEL

PASSAGE	*THEME*
Daniel 1:1-21	Daniel's First Days in Captivity
Daniel 2:1-49	Daniel's Interpretation of the King's Dreams
Daniel 3:1-30	The Golden Image and the Fiery Furnace
Daniel 5:1-31	Daniel's Interpretation of the Writing on the Wall
Daniel 6:1-28	The Plot Against Daniel and the Lion's Den
Daniel 9:1 – 12:13	Daniel's Vision of End Times

VERSES TO REMEMBER:	*Daniel 3:17-18*	*Stand for God*
	Daniel 9:19	*Prayer for the People of God*

HOSEA

PASSAGE	*THEME*
Hosea 1:1 – 3:5	Hosea's wife with an immoral past compared to Israel's sinful past
Hosea 6:1-3	Call to Revival
Hosea 11:1-12	God's Abiding Love for His People
Hosea 14:1-9	Call for Israel to return to God

VERSES TO REMEMBER:	*Hosea 6:6*	*God desires mercy, not sacrifice*
	Hosea 8:7	*Sow the wind, reap the whirlwind*
	Hosea 10:12	*Sow in righteousness, reap in mercy*
	Hosea 11:4	*God's draws man with bands of love*

JOEL

PASSAGE	*THEME*
Joel 1:13 – 2:17	Joel's Warning and Call to Repentance and Fasting
Joel 2:18-32	God's Promise of His Spirit and Restoration

VERSES TO REMEMBER:	*Joel 2:13*	*Characteristics of God*
	Joel 2:28-29	*The Outpouring of God's Spirit*

AMOS

VERSES TO REMEMBER: *Amos 4:12*   *Prepare to meet your God*
                          Amos 5:4   *Seek the Lord and you shall live*

Section 10 – REVIEW of DANIEL, HOSEA, JOEL and AMOS

DANIEL

1. What Babylonian name was given to Daniel in exile?_____

2. Match the Babylonian names of Daniel's three friends with their Israelite names:

   _____ Hananiah   A. Meshach

   _____ Mishael   B. Abednego

   _____ Azariah   C. Shadrach

3. Shadrach, Meshach and Abednego were thrown into the fiery furnace. Which did NOT happen?

   A. Their clothes were barely burned and they smelled like smoke
   B. The flames burned the men to death who threw them into the fiery furnace
   C. There was the appearance of a fourth man in the fire who looked like the Son of God

4. What was the writing on the wall that Daniel interpreted for the King Belshazzar?

   A. Mene Mene Tekel Peres
   B. Shadrach Meshach Abednego
   C. Lion Bear Leopard

5. King Darius made a decree which Daniel defied. For that, Daniel was thrown into:

   A. a filthy dungeon with seven other criminals
   B. a cage full of venomous snakes
   C. a cave full of lions

6. Daniel had a vision by the Hiddekel river in the third year of the reign of which king?_____

HOSEA

1. What was the name of Hosea's wife?_____

2. What were the names of Hosea's three children?

   (1)_____ (2)_____ (3)_____

61

3. According to Hosea 11:7, the people of God have a tendency to _____.

4. In Hosea 14:4, God says that he will _____.

JOEL

1. Joel tells God's people to sanctify a fast and call a solemn assembly.

True   /or/   False

2. When repentance occurs, God's people will experience the promise of:

    A. the outpouring of God's Spirit on all mankind
    B. the end of the prophetic period
    C. the termination of miracles

AMOS

1. The prophet Amos was from _____.

2. One of Israel's transgressions was the selling of the poor for a pair of shoes.

True   /or/   False

3. According to Amos 9:15, Israel will be returned to rebuild their land and:

    A. will never be free again
    B. will never be driven from their land again
    C. will never enjoy a good harvest again

DANIEL, HOSEA, JOEL, AMOS. Write the main facts, ideas and your personal thoughts on the books:

DANIEL:_____

HOSEA:_____

JOEL:_____

AMOS:_____

Section 11 – OBADIAH, JONAH, MICAH, NAHUM and HABAKKUK

OBADIAH

PASSAGE	THEME
Obadiah 17-21	Israel's Ultimate Triumph

VERSE TO REMEMBER: *Obadiah15* *Impending Judgment*

JONAH

PASSAGE	THEME
Jonah 1:1-2	Jonah's Call
Jonah 1:3 – 2:10	Jonah's Flight, Predicament and Prayer
Jonah 3:1-10	Jonah's Second Call and Nineveh's Repentance

VERSE TO REMEMBER: *Jonah 2:9* *Prayer of Passionate Gratitude*

MICAH

PASSAGE	THEME
Micah 2:1-11	Beware to those who oppress the poor
Micah 4:1-13	There will be a final Day of Peace and Redemption
Micah 5:1-15	Prophetic word about Bethlehem's man of Peace

VERSE TO REMEMBER: *Micah 6:8* *What the Lord requires of man*

NAHUM

PASSAGE	THEME
Nahum 1:15 – 3:19	The Overthrow of Judah's Oppressor (Nineveh)

VERSE TO REMEMBER: *Nahum 1:2-3* *Characteristics of God*

HABAKKUK

PASSAGE   _THEME_

Habakkuk 1:1 – 2:20   Injustice compared to Justice and Judgment

VERSE TO REMEMBER: _Habakkuk 2:4_   _The just shall live by faith_

Section 11 – REVIEW of OBADIAH, JONAH, MICAH, NAHUM and HABAKKUK

OBADIAH

1. Holiness and deliverance will be found on Mount _____.

JONAH

1. God called Jonah to go and preach against the sinfulness of what city?_____

2. Jonah disobeyed God by purchasing a trip to Tarshish and boarding a ship in:

    A. Joppa
    B. Japan
    C. Jersey

3. Who told the men on the ship to cast Jonah overboard in the midst of the storm?

    A. Jonah himself
    B. The captain of the ship
    C. Another prophet that was on board the ship

4. How long was Jonah in the belly of the great fish?

    A. 24 hours
    B. 60 minutes
    C. 3 days and 3 nights

5. The city of Nineveh rejected Jonah's message from God and refused to repent.

    True /or/   False

6. Jonah was greatly pleased when the people of Nineveh repented and God spared them.

    True /or/   False

MICAH

1. Micah was a prophet during the time of what three kings of Judah?

    (1)_____ (2)_____ (3)_____

2. Micah proclaims that in the last days weapons will be destroyed and war will cease.

        True   /or/   False

3. In Micah 6:8, what are the three requirements to do good?

    (1)_____

    (2)_____

    (3)_____

NAHUM

1. Nahum pronounces God's wrath and vengeance on:

    A. his adversaries and enemies
    B. the righteous remnant
    C. the poor and lowly masses

HABAKKUK

1. The prophet said that God would use the Corinthians and Colossians to possess the land of Israel.

        True   /or/   False

2. In a vision from God, Habakkuk pronounced that the just shall live by _____.

OBADIAH, JOHAH, MICAH, NAHUM, HABAKKUK. Write the main facts, ideas and your personal thoughts on the following books:

OBADIAH:_____

JONAH:_____

MICAH:_____

NAHUM:_____

HABAKKUK:_____

Section 12 – ZEPHANIAH, HAGGAI, ZECHARIAH and MALACHI

ZEPHANIAH

PASSAGE	*THEME*
Zephaniah 1:1 – 2:15	The scope of God's wrath and judgment
Zephaniah 3:1-20	Jerusalem's redemption and ultimate glory

> *VERSE TO REMEMBER:*   *Zephaniah 1:15*   *Judgment Day is a dark day indeed*

HAGGAI

PASSAGE	*THEME*
Haggai 1:1 – 2:9	Call to Reflect on Personal Wealth in contrast to the Dilapidated Temple

> *VERSES TO REMEMBER:*   *Haggai 1:5-7*   *Consider your ways*

ZECHARIAH

PASSAGE	*THEME*
Zechariah 1:7 – 6:8	The visions of Zechariah
Zechariah 7:8-10	How to treat those around you
Zechariah 9:9-17	Messianic prophecy

> *VERSE TO REMEMBER:*   *Zechariah4:6*   *Not by might or power but by God's Spirit*

MALACHI

PASSAGE	*THEME*
Malachi 1:6 – 2:17	Chastisement of the Priests
Malachi 3:1-15	Blessings of giving offerings and tithes

> *VERSES TO REMEMBER:*   *Malachi 2:5-6*   *Law and Covenant bring Life / Peace*
>   *Malachi 3:8-10*   *Bring the tithes to the storehouse*

Section 12 – REVIEW of ZEPHANIAH, HAGGAI, ZECHARIAH and MALACHI

ZEPHANIAH

1. Zephaniah was a prophet during the reign of _____, king of Judah.

2. In Zephaniah 1:15-18, the great day of the Lord is described as a beautiful, bright day for mankind.

    True   /or/   False

HAGGAI

1. Haggai was a prophet during the reign of King _____.

2. Haggai called the people of God to consider their priorities, because their houses were nice but the house of God was in great disrepair.

    True   /or/   False

ZECHARIAH

1. Zechariah was a prophet during the reign of King _____.

2. In Zechariah 4:6, it is "not by might, nor by power, but by _____, says the Lord of Hosts."

3. With the restoration of Jerusalem by God, Jerusalem shall be called a city of _____.

4. In Zechariah 9:9, the future King of Zion shall ride upon _____.

MALACHI

1. In Malachi 1:11, God reveals that even the _____ will worship him.

    a. Gentiles
    b. Generals
    c. Generations of Molech

2. God is the Lord and he:

    a. does not ever change.
    b. changes his commands from generation to generation.
    c. only changes when evil is great in the land.

3. Malachi challenges the people of God. He says they have robbed God by withholding their:

    a. love and affection to each other.
    b. wealth from the poor.
    c. tithes and offerings in God's house.

ZEPHANIAH, HAGGAI, ZECHARIAH, MALACHI. Write the main facts, ideas and your personal thoughts on the following books:

ZEPHANIAH:_____

_____

HAGGAI:_____

_____

ZECHARIAH:_____

_____

MALACHI:_____

_____

DIVISION FIVE
MATTHEW - MARK

Section 13 – MATTHEW chapters 1 – 10

MATTHEW 1 – 10

PASSAGE   *THEME*

Matthew 1:1-17   The genealogy of Jesus from Abraham to Joseph, Mary's husband
Matthew 1:18-25   The announcement of Jesus' birth to Joseph
Matthew 2:1-12   The birth of Jesus and visit by the wise men from the East
Matthew 2:13-23   The family's flight to Egypt and return to Nazareth
Matthew 3:1-17   The ministry of John the Baptist and the baptism of Jesus
Matthew 4:1-11   The temptation of Jesus by Satan in the wilderness
Matthew 4:12-25   The beginning of Jesus' ministry, first disciples and sudden fame
Matthew 5:1 – 7:29   The Sermon on the Mount
Matthew 8:1 – 9:8   Healing by Jesus
Matthew 9:9-13   The call of Matthew
Matthew 9:14-17   The question of fasting
Matthew 9:18-35   Healing by Jesus
Matthew 9:36 – 10:42   Laborers needed for the task, the call of the disciples, instructions

VERSES TO REMEMBER:
Matthew 4:29	The call to follow Jesus
Matthew 5:3-11	The Beatitudes
Matthew 5:16	Let your light so shine before men
Matthew 6:9-13	The Lord's Prayer
Matthew 6:33	Seek ye first the kingdom of God
Matthew 7:12	The Golden Rule
Matthew 9:37-38	Pray for laborers for the harvest
Matthew 10:2-4	The 12 disciples

Section 13 – REVIEW of MATTHEW chapters 1 – 10

MATTHEW 1 – 10

1. In Matthew's list of genealogy, what name begins the list in Matthew 1:2?_____

2. To whom did the angel first announce the birth of Jesus?

   A. Joseph
   B. Mary
   C. John the Baptist

3. In what city was Jesus born?_____

4. What was the name of the king in the Judean region?_____

5. What were the three gifts of the wise men when they arrived at the place where Jesus was?

   (1)_____

   (2)_____

   (3)_____

6. Who baptized Jesus?_____

7. How long did the temptation of Jesus in the wilderness last?

   A. 24 hours
   B. 3 days and 3 nights
   C. 40 days and 40 nights

8. Name the four fishermen who were the first to be called to follow Jesus:

   (1)_____

   (2)_____

   (3)_____

   (4)_____

9. The fame of Jesus spread quickly because of his ability to heal.

　　　True　　/or/　　False

10. In what is commonly referred to as the Sermon on the Mount, several Beatitudes are listed:

　　　Blessed are...

　　　(1) Matthew 5:3 　_____

　　　(2) Matthew 5:4 　_____

　　　(3) Matthew 5:5 　_____

　　　(4) Matthew 5:6 　_____

　　　(5) Matthew 5:7 　_____

　　　(6) Matthew 5:8 　_____

　　　(7) Matthew 5:9 　_____

　　　(8) Matthew 5:10 　_____

11. Jesus said that he came into the world to destroy and do away with the law of Moses.

　　　True　　/or/　　False

12. The topic of forgiveness is a part of the Lord's Prayer (or Model Prayer) in Matthew chapter 6.

　　　True　　/or/　　False

13. Jesus said that the "light of the body is the...

　　　A.　...mouth."
　　　B.　...eye."
　　　C.　...hair."

14. According to the teaching of Jesus in Matthew chapter 7, who shall enter into heaven?

　　　A.　Those who do the will of the Father in heaven.
　　　B.　Those who do many good works for the world to see.
　　　C.　Those who cry out publicly, "Lord, Lord."

15. While in a boat with his disciples, how did Jesus calm a raging storm that threatened their safety?

    A. He spoke and verbally rebuked the winds and the sea
    B. He prayed silently
    C. He told every disciple to pray fervently and loudly

16. In chapter 9, Jesus was able to...

    A. Fly to the moon.
    B. Run a mile in under four minutes.
    C. Heal disease, restore sight, cause the mute to speak and raise the dead.

17. From the list in chapter 10, name the 12 disciples:

    (1)_____

    (2)_____

    (3)_____

    (4)_____

    (5)_____

    (6)_____

    (7)_____

    (8)_____

    (9)_____

    (10)_____

    (11)_____

    (12)_____

18. In Matthew 10:5-8, the disciples were sent out to:

    (1) _____, saying "The kingdom of heaven is at hand."

    (2) _____ the sick

    (3) _____ the lepers

    (4) _____ the dead

    (5) _____ out devils

MATTHEW 1-10. Write the main facts, ideas and your personal thoughts on the book of Matthew 1-10:

_____

_____

_____

Section 14 – MATTHEW chapters 11 – 28

MATTHEW 11 – 28

PASSAGE	*THEME*
Matthew 11:1-19	The question of identity of Jesus and John the Baptist
Matthew 11:20-30	Coming judgment, wisdom and the Great Invitation
Matthew 12:1-8	Teachings concerning the Sabbath
Matthew 12:9-45	Healings, teachings and signs
Matthew 12:46-50	The question about who is Jesus' family
Matthew 13:1-58	Jesus' use of parables
Matthew 14:1-12	The beheading of John the Baptist
Matthew 14:13-36	Miraculous feeding, walking on water, calming storm, healing by Jesus
Matthew 15:1-20	Teaching about the things that defile
Matthew 15:21-39	Healings
Matthew 16:1-12	A wicked and adulterous generation looks for a sign
Matthew 16:13-28	Teachings on the foundation of the church, commitment and his death
Matthew 17:1-13	The transfiguration of Jesus
Matthew 17:14 – 18:20	Teachings on belief, greatness, temptation, evangelism and the church
Matthew 18:21 – 19:30	Teachings on forgiveness, divorce, attitudes on children and wealth
Matthew 20:1-16	Parable about those who come to "work in the vineyard"
Matthew 20:17-34	The final journey to Jerusalem, and the question of the disciples' rank
Matthew 21:1-16	Triumphal entry into Jerusalem and the cleansing of the Temple
Matthew 21:17 – 22:14	The authority of Jesus and his parables
Matthew 22:15-46	Questions about government, resurrection, the Great Commandment
Matthew 23:1 – 25:46	Pronouncement against religious leaders and unfaithfulness
Matthew 26:1-56	Betrayal, anointing, Last Supper, Garden of Gethsemane and arrest
Matthew 26:57 – 27:31	The trials and sentencing of Jesus
Matthew 27:32-66	The crucifixion and burial of Jesus
Matthew 28:1-20	The resurrection, appearance and Great Commission by Jesus

VERSES TO REMEMBER:

Matthew 11:28	*Come unto me, all that are burdened*
Matthew 16:16	*Peter's great confession of Jesus*
Matthew 19:26	*With God all things are possible*
Matthew 21:22	*Ask, believing, you shall receive*
Matthew 28:19-20	*The Great Commission*

Section 14 – REVIEW of MATTHEW chapters 11 – 28

1. Jesus said, "Come unto me, all you who labor and are heavy laden, and I will give you...

       A. ...a word of wisdom to comfort you."
       B. ...a vision of when your burdens will cease."
       C. ...rest."

2. Who is Lord of the sabbath day?_____

3. There was a man with a withered hand. What did Jesus ask him to do for healing to occur?

       A. Go to the temple and sacrifice.
       B. Simply stretch out his hand to Jesus.
       C. Go home and pray for healing.

4. According to Matthew 12:31, what is the only sin that cannot be forgiven?

       A. Blasphemy against the Holy Spirit.
       B. Blasphemy against the prophets and priests.
       C. Blasphemy against the preachers and teachers.

5. In Matthew 13:34, what kind of teaching and preaching did Jesus use to speak to the multitudes?

       A. Technical and theological terminology
       B. Highlights from the current news of the day
       C. Parables which needed explanation to some listeners

6. How did John the Baptist die?_____

7. The miraculous feeding of the 5,000 began with Jesus' prayer and blessing of:

       A. 5 loaves of bread and 2 fish
       B. 2 boatloads full of fresh fish
       C. 5 bushels of wheat

8. Both Jesus and Peter walked on water.

     True   /or/   False

9. Jesus asked the disciples who others thought he was. Who did they mention in their responses?

(1)_____

(2)_____

(3)_____

(4)_____

10. When asked by Jesus who they (the disciples) thought he was, Simon Peter answered:

_____

11. Which did NOT occur on the mountain when Jesus was transfigured?

A. The face of Jesus shone as the sun and his clothing became white as light
B. Moses and Elijah appeared and talked with Jesus
C. Jesus commanded the disciples to tell as many people as they could about this experience

12. In Matthew 18:3, how did Jesus explain greatness?

A. Whoever humbles himself as a little child
B. Whoever is able to perform numerous miracles
C. Whoever attends worship and does good deeds daily

13. A rich young ruler came to Jesus and asked about eternal life. In Matthew 19:21, Jesus gave his answer. What was the young man's response?

A. Exceeding great joy
B. Sorrowful
C. Confused

14. When Jesus entered into Jerusalem prior to his betrayal, which of the following is NOT a response of the people on the streets?

A. They spread garments and branches on the road for him to pass over
B. They shouted and sang "Hosanna to the Son of David"
C. They cursed him and asked him to leave their city

15. Jesus told the Pharisees that it was neither important nor needful to pay tribute to Caesar.

True   /or/   False

81

16. In Matthew 22:39, Jesus said that the second great commandment is to:

    A. Pay the tithes at all cost.
    B. Go to church every Sunday
    C. Love your neighbor as yourself.

17. In Matthew 24, Jesus speaks of the end of the world. Which of the following was NOT mentioned?

    A. Wars, famines, earthquakes, persecution of believers, false prophets
    B. The gospel preached to all the world, great tribulation, abominations, sun and moon darkened
    C. Repentance and revival of sinners, outpouring of love expressed to all Christians, joy and peace

18. The day of the end when the earth shall pass away can be known and predicted by Scripture.

    True   /or/   False

19. What was the name of the high priest who met with various ones to discuss the plot to kill Jesus?

    A. Simon
    B. Herod
    C. Caiaphas

20. Which disciple betrayed Jesus?_____

21. What was the name of the garden in which Jesus was arrested?_____

22. In Matthew 26:56, we find that all the disciples of Jesus were bold and stood by him during the trials.

    True   /or/   False

23. The High Priest accused Jesus of committing what crime?

    A. Theft
    B. Blasphemy
    C. Murder

24. Jesus was taken to stand trial before the governor of the region. What was his name?

    A. Pontias Pilate
    B. Peter the Pilot
    C. Hercules Poirot

25. Judas, the betrayer of Jesus, returned the 30 pieces of silver to the chief priests and:

    A. hanged himself
    B. escaped to a city of refuge
    C. rejoined the disciples

26. Pilate gave the people a choice to release a prisoner, either Jesus or _____.

27. Pilate's response to their choice: "I am _____ of the blood of this just person.

28. Which did NOT occur prior to the crucifixion of Jesus?

    A. They placed on him a scarlet robe, a crown of thorns and a reed in his right hand
    B. They mocked him, spit on him, hit him, stripped him and then clothed him again
    C. They gave him special and careful attention and offered him cool water to sip

29. On the day of the crucifixion, how many hours of darkness were there? _____

30. At the crucifixion, one of the centurions confessed:

    A. "Truly this was the Son of God."
    B. "Truly justice has been carried out this day."
    C. "Truly the priests of God are devout and holy."

31. A rich man of Arimathea came to Pilate and requested to bury the body of Jesus. His name was:

    A. Jeremiah
    B. Joseph
    C. Josiah

32. When Mary Magdalene and the other Mary came to the sepulcher, the stone had been rolled back. Who was sitting on the stone?

    A. Jesus
    B. The gardener
    C. An angel

33. The angel proclaimed, "He is not here, he is...

    A. ...risen."
    B. ...hiding."
    C. ...laying in another grave."

34. What was the first command to the women after seeing Jesus?

    A. Go and tell the disciples
    B. Go home and keep the resurrection a secret
    C. Go to the temple and tell the priests

35. What verbs did Jesus use in the Great Commission, found in Matthew 28:19?

    A. Run, hide and seek
    B. Eat, drink and be merry
    C. Go, teach and baptize

MATTHEW 11-28. Write the main facts, ideas and your personal thoughts on the book of Matthew 11-28:

_____

_____

_____

Section 15 – MARK

MARK

PASSAGE	THEME
Mark 1:1-11	The beginning of Jesus' ministry, baptism and wilderness temptation
Mark 1:12-20	The call of the four fisherman to be disciples
Mark 1:21 – 2:12	Miracles of demon expulsion, healing and preaching
Mark 2:13-14	The call of Levi (Matthew)
Mark 2:15-28	Ministry and teaching about sinners, fasting and the Sabbath
Mark 3:1-12	Healings
Mark 3:13-21	The naming of the 12 disciples
Mark 3:22-30	Teachings about the unpardonable sin and who is Jesus' family
Mark 4:1-41	The use of parables by Jesus
Mark 5:1 – 8:10	The ministry and miracles of Jesus, the beheading of John the Baptist
Mark 8:11-21	Pharisees' demand for a sign and Jesus' pronouncement of their sin
Mark 8:22-26	Healing by Jesus
Mark 8:27-30	The Great Confession by Peter
Mark 8:31 – 9:13	Jesus foretells his death and is transfigured
Mark 9:14-41	The powerlessness and discussion of greatness among the disciples
Mark 9:42 – 10:45	Teachings on sin, divorce, children, salvation, commitment, servant life
Mark 10:46-52	Healing of a blind man
Mark 11:1 – 13:37	Triumphal entry into Jerusalem, temple cleansing, final teachings
Mark 14:1 – 15:19	Plot, betrayal, trials and sentencing of Jesus
Mark 15:20 – 16:20	The crucifixion, burial, resurrection and Great Commission of Jesus

VERSES TO REMEMBER:	Mark 3:35	Those who do the will of God
	Mark 7:20-23	The things which defile a man
	Mark 9:23	If you believe, all things are possible
	Mark 13:31	God's Word will never pass away

Section 15 – REVIEW of MARK

MARK

1. Mark's account tells of John the Baptist and his eating habits. What two food items are mentioned specifically?

    A. locusts and wild honey
    B. camel meat and goat milk
    C. green olives and ripe figs

2. There were many who followed John the Baptist and were baptized in the river Jordan, and they were:

    A. ...desperate for food.
    B. ...confessing their sins.
    C. ...looking for fish.

3. When Jesus called four fishermen to be his followers, he said,

    "Come after me and I will make you...

    A. ...greater fishermen than all the other fishermen in the community."
    B. ...owners of a fleet of fishing boats."
    C. ...fishers of men."

4. Simon and Andrew were:

    A. brothers
    B. sisters
    C. uncle and nephew

5. James and John were:

    A. brothers, the sons of Zebedee
    B. cousins, the grandsons of Zebedee
    C. friends, neighbors of Zebedee

6. The first miracle that Mark describes is:

    A. walking on water
    B. flying in the air
    C. casting out an unclean spirit (demon) from a man

7. Jesus healed the _____ of Simon Peter from a deadly fever.

    A. wife
    B. mother-in-law
    C. daughter

8. In Mark 2:15, Jesus sat and spent time with many:

    A. sinners and publicans (corrupt government officials)
    B. high profile government officials from whom Jesus wanted help
    C. religious leaders to cultivate needed friendships

9. Jesus looked on the Pharisees with anger as he healed the man with the withered hand on the Sabbath.

       True   /or/   False

10. In Mark 3:13-19, Jesus ordained the twelve disciples to:

    (1)_____

    (2)_____

    (3)_____

11. Who is Jesus' family (brother, sister, mother)? Jesus gave an explanation. He said that it is:

    A. those who join a church
    B. those who attend the temple and offer sacrifices
    C. those who do the will of God

12. In the Gadarene country, a man with unclean spirits (demons) lived in a cemetery. Jesus healed him and the man wanted to follow Jesus. Jesus would not allow him, saying:

    A. Go home and tell others about the great things the Lord has done for you.
    B. Go away because you do not have enough faith.
    C. Go back home and get help from the governmental agencies.

13. Jesus grew up in Nazareth. Coming back to share his teaching and healing ministry, he:

    A. found unbelief and rejection
    B. was received with honor and fame
    C. was able to do mighty works of healing and miracles

14. Herod put John the Baptist in prison to appease:

    A. Philip, his brother
    B. his new wife, Herodias
    C. his daughter

15. After the feeding of the 5,000 people, how many baskets of leftover food fragments were filled?

    _____

16. In Mark 7:15-23, the things that defile man are not _____ but inward.

17. When Jesus healed the deaf man with a speech impediment, he told him to:

    A. tell only his friends
    B. tell everyone
    C. tell no one

18. The Pharisees questioned Jesus and demanded a sign from heaven. What did Jesus tell them?

    A. Come back in 3 days and you shall see a sign.
    B. No sign shall be given to this generation.
    C. You have been given a sign and you will understand it later.

19. The disciples were unable to heal a man's son. Jesus healed the boy. Jesus explained this power.

    A. This came by prayer and fasting.
    B. This came by special words of incantation.
    C. This came by a special type of touch and command.

20. At one point, the disciples had a dispute among themselves about who was the:

    A. most humble
    B. best friend of Jesus
    C. greatest

21. The Pharisees asked Jesus about divorce. He responded (Mark 10:8-9) that God's plan is:

    A. that the man and wife become "one flesh" in a union that God has joined together
    B. that the man and wife stay together in union until they desire to separate
    C. that the man and wife find a common goal to reach

22. How did the other ten disciples react when they heard the request by James and John for greatness?

    A. Excited
    B. Bored
    C. Displeased

23. Blind Bartimeus was healed by Jesus. After receiving his sight, he:

    A. followed Jesus.
    B. sat alone and cried.
    C. went home to celebrate.

24. Overthrowing the tables of the moneychangers in the temple, Jesus said that God's house must be:

    A. a house full of the poor
    B. a house of prayer
    C. a house of religious zealots

25. In Mark 12:37, which class of people listened to Jesus with glad hearts?

    A. the common people
    B. the royal family and court
    C. the religious leaders

26. What did Jesus say about the widow's small amount of money that she gave as an offering?

    A. The widow has given more than the rich because she gave all she had.
    B. The widow has much shame because she has so little to give.
    C. The widow will need to find financial assistance from family because she gave all.

27. A woman brought an alabaster box of ointment and poured in on the _____ of Jesus.

28. At the Passover with his disciples, Jesus broke the bread and said,

    "Take, eat, this is my _____."

29. Jesus told Peter that he (Peter) would deny Jesus three times. Peter's response:

    A. "There are too many of us for you to ever be taken and killed. I have no need to deny you."
    B. "I will not deny you in any way!"
    C. "My faith may be weak and I will most likely fall into fear and denial."

30. Jesus took three disciples with him to pray in the garden of Gethsemane. Name them:

   (1)_____

   (2)_____

   (3)_____

31. After denying Jesus three times, what was Peter's reaction to the cock crowing?_____

32. The crucifixion of Jesus took place at the place called _____, the place of a skull.

33. When Jesus died on the cross, what happened to the veil of the temple?

   A. The veil ripped in half starting from the top down to the bottom.
   B. Nothing happened to the veil.
   C. The veil ripped in half beginning at the bottom and going up to the top.

34. When the women returned from the grave of Jesus and said he had risen, the disciples believed them.

   True   /or/   False

35. After he commissioned the disciples to preach the gospel, Jesus ascended into heaven.

   True   /or/   False

MARK. Write the main facts, ideas and your personal thoughts on the book of Mark:

_____

_____

_____

DIVISION SIX
LUKE - JOHN

Section 16 – LUKE

LUKE

PASSAGE	THEME
Luke 1:1-56	Prophetic words concerning the births of John the Baptist and Jesus
Luke 1:57-80	The birth of John the Baptist
Luke 2:1-40	The birth and presentation of Jesus in the Temple
Luke 2:41-52	Jesus, 12 years old, in the Temple
Luke 3:1-22	The preaching of John the Baptist and the baptism of Jesus
Luke 3:23-38	The genealogy of Jesus beginning with Joseph going back to Adam
Luke 4:1-13	The temptation of Jesus in the wilderness
Luke 4:14 – 5:26	Teaching and healing by Jesus
Luke 5:27-29	The call of Levi (Matthew)
Luke 5:30 – 6:11	Question about Jesus' reputation and the Sabbath by the Pharisees
Luke 6:12-16	The naming of the 12 disciples
Luke 6:17 – 7:35	Teaching and healing by Jesus, with an explanation to John's disciples
Luke 7:36-40	The anointing of Jesus by a sinner
Luke 7:41 – 8:21	Teaching and the use of parables by Jesus
Luke 8:22-56	Miracles by Jesus – nature, demons, disease, death
Luke 9:1-17	The sending of the 12 disciples and the death of John the Baptist
Luke 9:18-62	Peter's Great Confession, the transfiguration and tests of discipleship
Luke 10:1-37	Sending and return of the 70 disciples, parable of the Good Samaritan
Luke 10:38 – 12:12	Teachings on priorities, prayer, unity and evil, Pharisees and fear
Luke 12:13 – 13:10	Teachings on priorities, worry, faithfulness, unity and repentance
Luke 13:11 – 18:14	Healings and teaching through use of parables by Jesus
Luke 18:15 – 19:27	Teachings about children, wealth, his death, salvation and stewardship
Luke 19:28 – 21:38	Jesus' entry into Jerusalem, temple cleansing, teachings and parables
Luke 22:1 – 23:25	The Last Supper, the betrayal, the trials and the sentencing of Jesus
Luke 23:26 – 24:53	Crucifixion, burial, resurrection, appearance and ascension of Jesus

VERSES TO REMEMBER:

	Luke 2:11	*Announcement of Christ's birth*
	Luke 5:31-32	*Jesus' call to sinners*
	Luke 6:38	*The principle of giving*
	Luke 9:23-26	*The terms of discipleship*
	Luke 9:57-62	*The tests of discipleship*
	Luke 12:34	*Your heart is where your treasure is*
	Luke 15:11-32	*The Prodigal Son*
	Luke 19:10	*Jesus came to seek and save the lost*

Section 16 – REVIEW of LUKE

LUKE

1. Luke's account of the gospel was written specifically to _____.

2. When the angel appeared to Zechariah, he was instructed to name his baby:

   _____

3. The name of the angel that appeared to Zechariah was _____.

4. Later, the angel Gabriel was sent to Nazareth to speak to a virgin named

   _____.

5. When Mary visited Elisabeth, the baby leaped in Elisabeth's womb and she was filled with the Spirit.

   True   /or/   False

6. Being struck dumb (not able to speak) was the sign of God's power to bring about birth in old age. When did Zechariah regain his ability to speak?

   A. When his son was born and he wrote down the instruction to name the boy John.
   B. When his friends named the boy Zechariah because it was his father's name.
   C. When his family arrived for the dedication ceremony of baby John.

7. Because of the tax decree, it was necessary for Joseph to travel to the city of _____.

8. The first people who heard the announcement of the birth of Jesus by the angel were:

   A. the wise men in a far country
   B. the servants in the king's household
   C. the shepherds in the fields nearby

9. After the days of purification, Jesus was brought to the city of _____ for presentation.

10. Simeon was a just, devout man who took Jesus in his arms and confirmed that Jesus was the Christ.

    True   /or/   False

11. After the Passover feast when he was 12, Jesus stayed behind in Jerusalem and was found:

   A. in the temple having discussion with the teachers and learned men
   B. in the courtyard playing games with his peers
   C. in the gardens inspecting the trees

12. In the fifteenth year of Tiberius Caesar, who were the three tetrarchs mentioned in Luke's gospel:

   (1) _____, tetrarch of Galilee

   (2) _____, tetrarch of Ituraea and the region of Trachonitis

   (3) _____, tetrarch of Abilene

13. At the baptism of Jesus by John, which of the following did NOT occur?

   A. Heaven opened up and the Holy Spirit descended in the bodily shape of a dove.
   B. A voice came from heaven and said, "You are my beloved Son; in you I am well pleased."
   C. Lightning and thunder appeared from nowhere and disappeared just as quickly.

14. In the genealogy of Jesus, the lineage is traced all way back to _____.

15. During the forty days of temptation in the wilderness, Jesus ate _____.

16. After the wilderness temptation, Jesus went to Galilee and taught in the _____.

17. In his hometown of Nazareth, Jesus taught in the synagogue. The people became angry and:

   A. led him to a hillside to throw him to his death.
   B. were comforted by his teaching.
   C. started a riot in the nearby town.

18. After the miracle of fish in the nets, Jesus asked the fishermen to follow him.

   True   /or/   False

19. Jesus said, "I came not to call the righteous, but _____ to repentance."

20. Immediately before calling the twelve disciples, Jesus went to a mountain to:

   A. sleep quietly.
   B. spend all night in prayer with God.
   C. wrestle with angels.

21. In Luke 6:37, Jesus commands his followers to:

    A. judge not, condemn not, and forgive
    B. examine, judge and condemn
    C. tempt, test and tell

22. The Pharisees condemned Jesus for allowing a woman to wash his feet with ointment because:

    A. the woman was well-known as a sinner
    B. the ointment was valuable and could have been given as an offering in the temple
    C. the Pharisees wanted to have their feet washed

23. Mary Magdalene was a woman that Jesus healed. How many demons were cast out of her?

    A. 3
    B. 7
    C. 13

24. After calming the storm on the lake with his disciples, he asked them a question:

    A. Where's the nearest shore?
    B. What time is it?
    C. Where is your faith?

25. When Jesus raised Jairus' twelve-year old daughter to life, who was allowed in the room?

    A. Peter, James, John and the parents (Jairus and his wife) of the girl
    B. Only Jairus
    C. Only the parents of the girl

26. In Luke 9:23, Jesus gives the terms of discipleship.

    He said, "If any man will come after me,

    (1) let him _____ himself, and

    (2) take up his _____ daily, and

    (3) _____ me."

27. In Luke chapter 10, Jesus sent out _____ disciples in groups of two.

28. In the parable of the Good Samaritan, who are the three individuals who came upon the wounded man who was left for dead?

    A. Prophet, priest, king
    B. Priest, Levite, Samaritan
    C. Hittite, Levite, Samaritan

29. What are the three commands that Jesus gives concerning prayer in Luke 11:9?

    A. Have faith, have hope, have love
    B. Hunt, peck, type
    C. Ask, seek, knock

30. According to Luke 12:31, if you seek the kingdom of God you will have your needs taken care of.

    True   /or/   False

31. When a woman was healed on the Sabbath day, the ruler of the synagogue became indignant because he believed that Jesus' miracle of healing was "work" which is not allowed on the Sabbath.

    True   /or/   False

32. What is the cost of discipleship, as found in Luke 14:27?

    (1) bear _____

    (2) come _____

33. Name the three parables found in Luke chapter 15:

    The parable of the lost _____

    The parable of the lost _____

    The parable of the lost _____

34. According to the words of Jesus in Luke 17:4, how many times must we forgive others?

    (1) As many times as others sin against us
    (2) Only once
    (3) It depends on whether the offender asks for forgiveness

35. In Luke 17:5, what did the disciples ask for? _____

36. Zaccheus, when he met with Jesus, promised to:

    A. give half of his goods to the poor and repay four times the amount to those he cheated.
    B. never cheat in his tax collecting duties again.
    C. give a percentage to Jesus' ministry.

37. On the day of his entry into Jerusalem, Jesus was told to reprimand his disciples because of their vocal praise of him. He responded:

    A. "If they kept quiet, the stones would immediately cry out!"
    B. "I cannot reprimand them because they are not of my following."
    C. "Please join them in our great celebration."

38. Jesus taught about the resurrection of the faithful. He said that there is no marriage in heaven.

    True   /or/   False

39. Who did Jesus send to prepare the Last Supper of the Passover meal?

    A. Mutt and Jeff
    B. Peter and John
    C. Judas and Ananias

40. While Jesus prayed in the garden before the betrayal, who appeared from heaven to strengthen him?

    A. Elijah
    B. Moses
    C. An angel

41. Before Jesus was sentenced, he was brought to answer charges in three separate locations:

    A. Jerusalem, Athens, Rome
    B. Home, Temple, Stadium
    C. High Priest's house, Council of elders and chief priests and scribes, Pilate

42. What were the crimes of Barabbas?

    A. Insurrection and murder
    B. Petty theft and fraud
    C. Vagrancy and impersonation

43. While Jesus hung on the cross dying, what did the soldiers offer him to drink?_____

44. Was Jesus laid in a new grave or old grave?_____

45. What was the name of one of Jesus' followers who was walking on the road to Emmaus in Chapter 24 of Luke?

    A. Cleopatra
    B. Cleopas
    C. Claudius

46. After his resurrection but prior to his ascension, what did Jesus eat?

    A. fish and honeycomb
    B. fish and chips
    C. fish and bread

LUKE. Write the main facts, ideas and your personal thoughts on the book of Luke:

_____

_____

_____

_____

Section 17 – JOHN

JOHN

PASSAGE	THEME
John 1:1-5	Jesus is the Word, the life and the light of man
John 1:6-51	John the Baptist's testimony of Jesus and the call of the first disciples
John 2:1-12	The first miracle of Jesus
John 2:13-25	The cleansing of the temple
John 3:1-21	The meeting between Jesus and Nicodemus about the new birth
John 3:22-36	John the Baptist confirms the deity of Jesus
John 4:1 – 5:47	The ministry of relationship and the teachings and healings of Jesus
John 6:1-65	The miracle of feeding 5,000, walking on water and teaching of Jesus
John 6:66-71	Peter's Great Confession
John 7:1-53	Public opinion was divided over Jesus
John 8:1-30	Jesus forgives an adulteress
John 8:31-59	Abraham's true descendants and the place of Jesus before Abraham
John 9:1 – 10:21	Healings and teachings of Jesus
John 10:22-42	Jesus' claim of divinity
John 11:1-46	Jesus raises Lazarus from the dead
John 11:47 – 12:50	The Pharisees reaction, anointing of Jesus, last entrance to Jerusalem
John 13:1 – 16:15	Last teachings of Jesus – humility, betrayal, salvation, Holy Spirit
John 16:16-33	Teachings on joy and victory
John 17:1-26	Jesus' prayer for his disciples
John 18:1 – 19:15	The betrayal, arrest, trials and sentencing of Jesus
John 19:16 – 20:25	The crucifixion, burial, resurrection and appearance of Jesus

VERSES TO REMEMBER:

John 1:1	*In the beginning was the Word*
John 3:5	*The new birth*
John 3:16	*Belief in Jesus brings everlasting life*
John 4:24	*We must worship in spirit and in truth*
John 6:35	*Jesus is the bread of life*
John 8:31-32	*The truth shall make you free*
John 10:30	*I and the Father are one*
John 11:35	*The shortest verse in the Bible*
John 13:35	*The world will know us by our love*
John 14:1	*Let not your heart be troubled*
John 14:6	*I am the Way, the Truth and the Life*
John 14:15	*How to show love for the Lord*
John 15:1-8	*Abiding in the Lord, bearing fruit*
John 20:29	*Believers who have not seen blessed*

Section 17 – REVIEW of JOHN

JOHN

1. What divine purpose in life did John the Baptist have?

    A. To be the Light of the world
    B. To bear witness of the Light of men
    C. To hide the Light of glory

2. In John 1:14, we find that "the Word was made _____."

3. The law was given by Moses, but grace and truth came by:

    A. The church
    B. The disciples
    C. Jesus Christ

4. Andrew first heard the message about Jesus and ran to find his brother named _____.

5. The first recorded miracle in the gospel of John occurred at a marriage in _____.

6. Jesus told Nicodemus that, to have everlasting life, one must:

    A. Believe in God's only son
    B. Do good works
    C. Be kind to one another

7. The Pharisees heard that Jesus had more disciples (followers) than John the Baptist.

    True   /or/   False

8. How many disciples did Jesus baptize?

    A. None – however, his disciples did baptize other followers
    B. 5,000 men, not counting women and children
    C. Several hundred before being ordered to cease and desist

9. Jesus told the Samaritan woman at the well in Sychar that God is to be worshipped...

    A. in the confines of the temple or synagogue.
    B. in open spaces of the desert regions.
    C. in spirit and in truth.

10. Jesus healed a man who was laying by the pool of Bethesda. How many years had he been crippled?

   A. 38
   B. 18
   C. 8

11. In John 5:27, Jesus says that God the Father has given him authority to _____.

12. After the feeding of the 5,000 the multitude wanted to take Jesus by force to make him _____.

13. In John 6:35, Jesus describes himself as the _____ of life.

14. When an adulteress was brought to Jesus, he was asked if she should be stoned to death.

   He replied:

   A. "If there is one here without sin, let him cast the first stone at her."
   B. "Do not stone her alone, but bring the other sinner here as well."
   C. "You may stone her, but not to the point of death."

15. Jesus made a significant statement about himself. He said, "Before Abraham was, _____."

16. If an individual confessed that Jesus was the Christ, they were...

   A. stoned to death
   B. given special privileges by their families
   C. excluded from participating in the synagogue

17. Jesus made another statement which angered the Jews: "I and my Father are _____."

18. What does John 11:35 say:_____

19. Jesus spoke three words to bring Lazarus to life from the grave:

   A. "Death, be conquered!"
   B. "Lazarus, come forth!"
   C. "Everybody, stay away!"

20. Because of the fame, the chief priests consulted and plotted to kill Lazarus as well as Jesus.

   True   /or/   False

21. In John 12:20, what was the nationality of the individuals who came and wanted to see Jesus?

    A. Greeks
    B. Geeks
    C. Freaks

22. Who put it into the heart of Judas Iscariot to betray Jesus?_____

23. After the Last Supper, Jesus began to wash:

    A. dishes
    B. the disciples' feet
    C. his clothes

24. Jesus told his disciples, "The world will know you are my disciples if…

    A. …you have love one for another."
    B. …you are able to copy my miracles."
    C. …you start many churches."

25. Jesus said, "If I go,…I will…

    A. …never return."
    B. …come again."
    C. …disappear."

26. Jesus told his disciples (John 14:15): "If you love me, keep my _____."

27. In John 15:14, Jesus calls the disciples his _____.

28. In John 16:7, Jesus said that when he departs, he will send the _____.

29. In John 17:20, Jesus prayed not only for the disciples present but also for…

    A. those who believe on Jesus because of their witness.
    B. those who pray to other gods.
    C. those who follow Satan.

30. When Jesus was arrested in the garden, Simon Peter took a sword and…

    A. stabbed Judas Iscariot.
    B. had a duel with one of the guards.
    C. cut off the right ear of Malchus, the servant of the high priest.

31. In John 18:38, Pilate asked a profound question of Jesus. What was that question?

    A. "What is the beginning of life?"
    B. "Who has the keys of the kingdom?"
    C. "What is truth?"

32. Again, in John 18:38, what was Pilate's verdict about Jesus which he announced to the Jews?

    A. "I find absolutely no fault in him."
    B. "He is guilty of treason to the nation of Israel."
    C. "I find in him the offense of heresy and false teaching."

33. What title did Pilate give Jesus to be put on the cross?

    A. Jesus of Nazareth, King of the Jews
    B. Jesus, the Liar of the North
    C. Jesus, the Lunatic of the Kingdom

34. The final words of Jesus, as he died on the cross:

    A. "It is finished."
    B. "It is a hot day in Hades."
    C. "It is only the beginning."

35. A soldier pierced the side of Jesus with his spear. What came forth from Jesus' body?

    A. Vinegar
    B. Salt water
    C. Blood and water

36. Simon Peter and another disciple (John) raced to the empty tomb. Who stopped at the door and did not enter?

    A. Simon Peter
    B. The other disciple (John)
    C. Mary Magdalene

37. Mary Magdalene looked in the tomb and saw _____ angels.

38. Mary saw Jesus but did not recognize him at first. She thought he was the...

    A. guard
    B. gardener
    C. grandson of the high priest

39. Thomas did not believe that Jesus had resurrected. He said that he needed proof by...

    A. seeing and touching the nail prints in Jesus' hands and touching his pierced side
    B. talking face to face with Jesus
    C. examining the garments of Jesus

40. How many fish were caught when Jesus appeared to the disciples at the sea of Tiberias?_____

41. What repetitious phrase did Jesus use in John 21:17 as a command to Simon Peter?

    A. "Feed the poor."
    B. "Feed the lonely."
    C. "Feed my sheep."

JOHN. Write the main facts, ideas and your personal thoughts on the book of John:

_____

_____

_____

_____

DIVISION SEVEN
ACTS - ROMANS

Section 18 — ACTS chapters 1 – 9

ACTS 1-9

PASSAGE

THEME

Passage	Theme
Acts 1:1-11	The Commission to Evangelize
Acts 1:12 – 2:4	The Upper Room on the Day of Pentecost
Acts 2:5-41	The Preaching of Peter on the Day of Pentecost
Acts 2:42-47	The Lifestyle of the Believers in the Early Church
Acts 3:1-26	The healing of the lame man and Peter's message about repentance
Acts 4:1-22	The imprisonment and release of Peter and John
Acts 4:23 – 5:16	Signs and Wonders by the Apostles
Acts 5:17-42	Imprisonment, Release by an Angel, and Teaching at the Temple Daily
Acts 6:1-7	Appointment of the Seven to minister with Apostles
Acts 6:8 – 7:60	Arrest and martyrdom of Stephen
Acts 8:1 – 9:31	The conversion of Saul, who is renamed Paul
Acts 9:32-43	Miracles by the apostles

VERSES TO REMEMBER: *Acts 1:8*   *You shall receive power*
Acts 4:12   *No other name in heaven for salvation*

Section 18 – REVIEW of ACTS chapters 1 – 9

ACTS 1 – 9

1. The book of Acts (Acts 1:1) and the gospel of Luke (Luke 1:3) were written to:

        A. Theophilus
        B. Theodore
        C. Thessalonica

2. At the ascension, what geographical locations were mentioned as places to be witnesses for Christ?

        (1)_____

        (2)_____

        (3)_____

        (4)_____

3. What two men were named as choices to replace Judas as one of the twelve apostles?

        (1)_____

        (2)_____

4. Who was selected to be the twelfth apostle after the resurrection of Jesus?

5. What was the miraculous ability of the apostles when they were filled with the Holy Spirit on Pentecost, as found in Acts 2:8-11?

        A. The disciples were able to speak with their hair on fire.
        B. The disciples were able to speak about God in every dialect and language of those present.
        C. The disciples were able to speak in complete sentences.

6. With the gathered crowd asking questions, who stood up boldly to give an answer and preach?

        A. Peter
        B. James
        C. John

7. On the very day that Peter preached, how many were added to the number of believers?_____

8. In Acts 2:44-45, what was the attitude towards possessions and wealth of the believers?

   A. The believers worked harder to gain more wealth for the impending persecution.
   B. The believers walked away from all their possessions to wait for the coming of Jesus.
   C. The believers held all things common, sold their possessions, shared with those in need.

9. Peter and John went to the temple to pray and saw a crippled man lying at the gate called Beautiful.

   A. Peter said that he had no money but he would come back later to help.
   B. John told the man to ask him family for more assistance.
   C. Peter commanded the man to stand up and walk -- then lifted the man up by the right hand.

10. According to Acts 4:10-12, how many different ways to heaven (or salvation) are there?

    A. Just one – only by the name of Jesus Christ of Nazareth
    B. Unlimited – any way within the imagination of man will be helpful to reach heaven
    C. None – there is no way for man to find righteousness and salvation

11. In Acts 4:31, the believers prayed as they assembled together in one accord. The place shook and:

    A. they were all filled with the Holy Spirit and proclaimed the Word of God with boldness.
    B. they were all frightened and waited for the earthquake to pass.
    C. they were all thrown to the ground but miraculously uninjured.

12. Being filled with the Spirit, the believers also...

    A. sold their possessions, brought the money to the apostles for distribution to those in need.
    B. asked the poorest of the new converts to work in the homes of the wealthy as servants
    C. openly shared their disagreements in love.

13. Ananias and Sapphira sold property, brought a portion to the apostles as if it were the whole amount.

    A. Both were struck down dead because of their deception against the Spirit of God.
    B. Both were thanked graciously for the generosity.
    C. Both were ignored and allowed to worship with the congregation.

14. According to Acts 5:18, the apostles were thrown into prison because of the high priest and others.

    True   /or/   False

15. Who opened the prison doors, released the apostles and set them free during the night?

    A. The chief jailer
    B. The other believers in the church
    C. An angel

16. When released, what did the apostles do?

    A. They went home to rest and pray.
    B. They went directly to the temple and began to teach the people openly.
    C. They went into hiding

17. Peter's famous response to the council: "We ought to obey God rather than _____."

18. The council listened to the wisdom of:

    A. The chief priest
    B. Gamaliel
    C. Saul of Tarsus

19. To assist in ministering to the needs of the believers, the apostles asked for the names of men who had high reputations, who were full of wisdom and the Spirit of God. Name the seven men:

    (1)_____

    (2)_____

    (3)_____

    (4)_____

    (5)_____

    (6)_____

    (7)_____

20. Which one of the chosen seven was the first to be stoned to death as a martyr?_____

21. In Acts 8:1, a man is mentioned as part of the consenting crowd who killed Stephen. His name:

    A. Saul, who later became the apostle Paul
    B. Simon, who was also known as Peter
    C. James, the son of Zebedee

22. Philip read the Scriptures and preached Jesus to the eunuch of Ethiopia. What was the eunuch's job?

    A. Chief treasurer of Candace the queen of Ethiopia
    B. Chief housekeeper in the palace of the queen
    C. Chief cook in the palace of the Pharaoh in Egypt

23. The eunuch desired to be baptized. What was the requirement for baptism, according to Philip?

    A. "If you can explain your salvation experience and join a church, you may be baptized."
    B. "If you believe with all your heart, you can be baptized."
    C. "If you tithe and find a place to work in the ministry, you will be considered for baptism."

24. Saul's conversion experience happened on the road to what city?

    A. Decapolis
    B. Dallas
    C. Damascus

25. Saul, at his conversion, was made blind and did not eat or drink for how many days?

    A. 40 days
    B. 3 days
    C. 14 days

26. The Lord spoke to Ananias in a vision about Saul's conversion. What was Ananias' first reaction?

    A. "Lord, this man has an evil reputation because of his persecution of the believers."
    B. "Lord, this man has no place in the houses of the saints. He cannot be saved."
    C. "Lord, please find someone else to help this evil man Saul. I refuse to help him."

27. God's reply to Ananias was: "Saul is now...

    A. ...just like another Judas Iscariot."
    B. ...my chosen vessel."
    C. ...your best friend."

28. Because of his preaching, Saul became a hunted man by the Jews. He escaped and went back to:

    A. Tarsus
    B. Jerusalem
    C. Babylon

29. Peter raised a young woman named Tabitha (translated to Dorcas) to life from the dead.

     True   /or/   False

ACTS 1-9. Write the main facts, ideas and your personal thoughts on the book of Acts 1-9:

_____

_____

_____

_____

Section 19 – ACTS chapters 10 – 28

ACTS 10 – 28

PASSAGE	THEME
Acts 10:1-48	Peter's preaching to, conversion of and Holy Spirit filling of Gentiles
Acts 11:1-18	Contention and resolution in the Early Church over Gentile conversion
Acts 11:19-30	Persecution helps spread the Gospel
Acts 12:1-19	Death and Imprisonment of apostles with Peter's release by an Angel
Acts 13:1 – 14:28	Paul's missionary journey from Antioch
Acts 15:1-33	Dissension and resolution again in the Early Church in Jerusalem
Acts 16:19-40	Imprisonment and miraculous release, with the jailer coming to faith
Acts 17:16-34	Paul's preaching in Athens on second missionary journey
Acts 19:1 – 21:26	Paul's third missionary journey with preaching, trouble and warnings
Acts 21:27 – 23:22	Paul's arrest and trial by Jewish council
Acts 23:23 – 24:27	Paul sent to governor Felix for trial
Acts 25:1-12	Paul stands before Festus and appeals to Caesar
Acts 25:13 – 26:32	Paul's case is taken to King Agrippa who listens to Paul's conversion
Acts 27:1-44	Paul placed on ship bound for Rome, shipwreck occurs
Acts 28:1-31	Miracles by Paul, then final passage to Rome and imprisonment

VERSES TO REMEMBER: *Acts 16:30-31* *What one must do to be saved*
Acts 26:28 *Almost is not quite good enough*

Section 19 – REVIEW of ACTS chapters 10 – 28

ACTS 10 – 28

1. An angel appeared to Cornelius to ask Peter to come to Caesarea. Cornelius was...

    A. a musician in the Jerusalem band
    B. a centurion of the Italian band
    C. a priest in the Jesuit band

2. Before being summoned by Cornelius, the vision of Peter was about...

    A. the regulations of food (clean and unclean) and the new freedom to eat all meats
    B. the strength of a sheet with four corners bound tight
    C. the Macedonian call to missionary work

3. The people in Caesarea were Gentiles. When Peter preached to them,...

    A. the gift of the Holy Spirit was poured out on the Gentiles and they spoke in different languages.
    B. the Gentiles were hardened in their hearts because of their cultural background.
    C. the Jewish Christians would not allow the Gentiles to convert and be baptized.

4. In Acts 11:1-2, the Jewish believers were joyful and ecstatic that Peter had gone to the Gentiles.

    True   /or/   False

5. Barnabas was sent to see the Gentile converts in Antioch. He brought Saul of Tarsus there.

    A. It was in Antioch that the believers were first called Christians.
    B. It was in Antioch that great heresies were taught by the first converts.
    C. It was in Antioch that Barnabas was greatly distressed and disappointed in the new converts.

6. The apostle James was killed by King Herod, who then imprisoned the apostle _____.

7. There were _____ soldiers attached to Peter after his arrest.

8. Peter was awakened in prison, his chains fell off and he was escorted out through the front gate by...

    A. John, the brother of James
    B. an angel of the Lord
    C. several converts from Antioch

9. Who left Peter standing at the door of the house where Christian believers were praying?

    A. Rhoda
    B. Mary the mother of John
    C. John whose surname was Mark

10. Which two men were sent out by the church in Antioch to preach and minister abroad?

    A. Barnabas and Saul
    B. Simeon and Manaen
    C. Lucius and Mark

11. In Acts 13:9, the Scripture notes that Saul has another name now. What is that name?

    A. Solomon
    B. Paul
    C. Salucius

12. After preaching to the Jews in Antioch of Pisidia on the Sabbath, they preached the next week to:

    A. nearly the entire city who gathered to listen to the Word of God.
    B. only the Gentiles.
    C. only the Jewish congregation again.

13. There were Pharisees in Jerusalem who were converts. They felt Gentile converts needed:

    A. to send more financial money to Jerusalem.
    B. to move closer to the land of Judah.
    C. to be circumcised and fully obedient to the law of Moses.

14. The council agreed with a judgment that released the Gentile converts from the burden of circumcision.

    True   /or/   False

15. The Gentile believers were commanded to abstain from all of the following EXCEPT:

    A. marriage
    B. meats offered to idols and the meat of strangled animals
    C. fornication and eating blood

16. Paul and Silas were thrown into prison in the city of _____ where Lydia became a believer.

17. When Paul and Silas prayed in the jail, the earth shook and all the prison doors were opened.

    A. Paul and Silas stayed in their cell even though the prison doors were opened.
    B. Paul and Silas escaped and fled the country.
    C. Paul and Silas immediately ran to the house of Lydia.

18. In Thessalonica, the unbelieving Jews attacked the house of a convert named _____.

19. Paul stood on _____ in Athens to proclaim the gospel of Jesus.

20. After Paul left Athens, he then went to _____.

21. In Acts 19, Paul spoke to the believers in Ephesus. They were baptized again, this time...

    A. in the name of John the Baptist.
    B. in the name of Paul the Apostle.
    C. in the name of Jesus the Lord.

22. In Acts 20, Paul traveled to Macedonia to minister and then he spent 3 months in _____.

23. The elders of the Ephesian church came to Miletus at Paul's request. After speaking to them:

    A. Paul turned his face from them and walked away.
    B. Paul knelt down and prayed with them all.
    C. Paul commissioned them all to be missionaries abroad.

24. Paul was dragged from the temple in Jerusalem and arrested. He was allowed by the chief captain of the soldiers to speak in defense of his arrest on the steps of the palace. He preached:

    A. And shared his conversion experience in detail
    B. Greek theology
    C. Roman mythology

25. According to Acts 23:8, what were the theological differences between the Pharisees and Sadducees?

    A. The Sadducees did not believe in the resurrection, in angels or spirits – the Pharisees did.
    B. The Pharisees believed in the Mosaic law – the Sadducees did not.
    C. The Sadducees did not believe in Jesus as the Messiah – the Pharisees did.

26. Paul was sent to stand before the governor in Caesarea, whose name was _____.

27. Who replaced Felix as governor in Caesarea?_____

28. Governor Festus was visited by King Agrippa, who agreed to hear Paul's case. In Acts 26:28, what was Agrippa's response to Paul's testimony of conversion and gospel message of Jesus the Christ?

    A. Agrippa said, "Paul, you are a fool."
    B. Agrippa said, "Paul, I believe and desire to be baptized."
    C. Agrippa said, "Paul, you have almost persuaded me to be a Christian."

29. Festus and Agrippa agreed that Paul was to be sent to appeal his case to Caesar in Rome.

    True   /or/   False

30. Paul's boat was shipwrecked and all swam to shore. They landed on the island of _____.

31. Putting a bundle of wood on a bonfire, Paul was bitten by a venomous snake. Paul shook off the snake, had no swelling and did not die. Because of that, the people believed Paul was:

    A. a snake charmer
    B. a god.
    C. a doctor.

32. Paul arrived in Rome and called a meeting with the Jews there. He preached Jesus to them and:

    A. they all believed.
    B. some believed and some did not believe.
    C. no one believed the gospel message.

ACTS 10-28. Write the main facts, ideas and your personal thoughts on the book of Acts 10-28:

_____

_____

_____

_____

Section 20 – ROMANS

ROMANS

PASSAGE   *THEME*

Romans 1:1-16   Paul's readiness to preach and encourage believers in Rome
Romans 1:17 – 3:20   The guilt and sin of mankind
Romans 3:21 – 5:21   Justification and Salvation
Romans 6:1-23   Grace, freedom and the abundant life
Romans 7:1 – 8:39   The struggle of the two natures, but we are conquerors through Christ
Romans 10:4-17   Righteousness comes by faith alone
Romans 12:1 – 13:14   How to live the abundant life of faith with those around you
Romans 15:1-6   Unity in Christ glorifies the Father

VERSES TO REMEMBER: *Romans 1:16*   *I am not ashamed of the Gospel*
                          Romans 8:38   *What separates us from God's love?*
                          Romans 10:9-13   *How to be saved*
                          Romans 12:1-2   *Be transformed by God's renewing*
                          Romans 13:10   *Love is the fulfillment of the law*
                          Romans 15:4   *Why we need the Scriptures*

Section 20 – REVIEW of ROMANS

ROMANS

1. The author of the book of Romans is _____.

2. Paul felt ashamed of the gospel as he was brought to Rome as a prisoner.

    True   /or/   False

3. In Romans 1:26-31, Paul presents a list of the many sins of the ungodly. Name 10 from his list:

    (1)_____

    (2)_____

    (3)_____

    (4)_____

    (5)_____

    (6)_____

    (7)_____

    (8)_____

    (9)_____

    (10)_____

4. According to Romans 3:23, who (among all the earth) is sinless?

    A. No one because all have sinned
    B. Only the high priest who has access to the Holy of Holies
    C. Everyone because no one sins due to the relative nature of good and evil

5. From Romans 5:1, how do we find peace with God?

    A. By doing good deeds daily
    B. By justification of our faith in Jesus Christ
    C. By memorizing Scripture verses

6. In Romans 5:8, we see that God loved us enough to send Christ to die for us.

   True   /or/   False

7. If we have full forgiveness through our faith in Jesus, should we continue to purposefully sin to receive and increase the grace that God provides?

   Yes   /or/   No

8. According to Romans 6:23, what is the end result (payment) for sin?

   A. Pleasure
   B. Life
   C. Death

9. The struggle of the two natures is found in Romans 7:22-23. How does Paul describe it?

   A. As the personal delight in the law of God waging war against the captivity of the mind in sin
   B. As the depiction of one devil wrestling with another devil
   C. As a picture of demons waging battle with angels

10. The believer does not receive the spirit of bondage but rather the Spirit of _____.

11. Paul is confident in his salvation and says, "For I am persuaded that...

   (1) ...neither _____,

   (2) ...nor _____,

   (3) ...nor _____,

   (4) ...nor _____,

   (5) ...nor _____,

   (6) ...nor _____,

   (7) ...nor _____,

   (8) ...nor _____,

   (9) ...nor _____,

   (10)...nor _____,

   ...shall be able to separate us from the love of God, which is in Christ Jesus our Lord."

12. Romans 10:9 states that you can be saved if...

    (1) ...you confess with your _____ the Lord Jesus, and

    (2) ...believe in your _____ that God has raised him from the dead."

13. Who is denied the opportunity to be saved, according to Romans 10:13?

    A. No one, because the "whosoever" includes everyone in the world.
    B. Those who never attend church.
    C. The rich and powerful, because of their elitist attitudes.

14. In Romans 10:17, how does faith come to an individual?

    A. By taking classes from spiritual leaders.
    B. By a special visit from God through visions and dreams.
    C. By hearing the Word of God.

15. In Romans 12:1, Paul calls the believers to present themselves as a:

    (1) _____

    (2)_____

    (3)_____

16. In Romans 12:2, we are to be:

    A. transformed by renewing, not conformed by the world
    B. confirmed, not confounded
    C. translated, not elated

17. According to Romans 12:10, we should always put ourselves first and foremost.

    True   /or/   False

18. We are called to bless, not curse, those who persecute us as believers.

    True   /or/   False

19. From Romans 13:10, we find out how to fulfill the law. What fulfills the law?

    A. Hope
    B. Faith
    C. Love

20. In his closing remarks (Romans 16:17), Paul tells us who to avoid:

    A. losers
    B. winners
    C. those who cause divisiveness and sin

ROMANS. Write the main facts, ideas and your personal thoughts on the book of Romans:

_____

_____

_____

DIVISION EIGHT
1 CORINTHIANS - COLOSSIANS

Section 21 – 1 CORINTHIANS and 2 CORINTHIANS

1 CORINTHIANS

PASSAGE	THEME
1 Corinthians 1:1 – 2:13	Paul speaks against the divisions in the church
1 Corinthians 2:14 – 4:5	The carnal man contrasted to the spiritual man, a co-laborer with Christ
1 Corinthians 4:6-21	The authority of spiritual apostleship and leadership
1 Corinthians 5:1 – 8:13	The standards of Christian living
1 Corinthians 9:1-27	Rights and obligations of Christian leadership
1 Corinthians 10:1-33	Flee from temptation and do all to the glory of God
1 Corinthians 11:1-34	Teaching concerning women and the Lord's Supper
1 Corinthians 12:1-31	Teaching concerning spiritual gifts
1 Corinthians 13:1-13	The way of love is greatest
1 Corinthians 14:1-40	Teachings concerning the issue of tongues and worship
1 Corinthians 15:1-58	The resurrection of Christ is central to our faith

VERSES TO REMEMBER:

1 Corinthians 1:18	*The preaching of the cross*
1 Corinthians 3:9	*We are laborers together with God*
1 Corinthians 6:20	*We are bought with a price*
1 Corinthians 10:13	*You will not be tempted above ability*
1 Corinthians 10:31	*Do all to the glory of God*
1 Corinthians 16:13	*Stand fast in the faith*

2 CORINTHIANS

PASSAGE	THEME
2 Corinthians 1:3-11	Sufferings and afflictions
2 Corinthians 2:5-11	The power of forgiveness
2 Corinthians 5:1-21	Christians are the ministers of reconciliation in the world
2 Corinthians 6:1-10	Paul's reflection on how he serves in ministry
2 Corinthians 6:11 – 7:16	Call to separation, holiness and repentance
2 Corinthians 8:1 – 9:15	The proof of the sincerity of love is through giving
2 Corinthians 12:1-10	Paul's thorn in the flesh

VERSES TO REMEMBER:

2 Corinthians 1:4	*Comforted by God to comfort others*
2 Corinthians 4:8-9	*No despair in outward troubles*
2 Corinthians 5:7	*We walk by faith, not by sight*
2 Corinthians 5:17	*We are a new creation in Christ*

Section 21 – REVIEW of 1 CORINTHIANS and 2 CORINTHIANS

1 CORINTHIANS

1. Paul confirms that he was called as an _____ of Jesus Christ.

2. Paul, in his usual manner, uses the words "grace" and "peace" as he begins his letter.

    True   /or/   False

3. In 1 Corinthians 1:9, Paul states unequivocally that God is _____.

4. The preaching of the cross is:

    A. foolishness to unbelievers but it is the power of God to believers.
    B. unnecessary.
    C. a waste of time.

5. According to 1 Corinthians 2:16, believers have:

    A. much persecution to endure.
    B. more fun than a barrel of monkeys.
    C. the mind of Christ.

6. Christians are not to be in competition with each other, but rather laborers together with God.

    True   /or/   False

7. Because the Spirit of God dwells in the believer, the believer's body is the _____ of God.

8. In 1 Corinthians 4:2, we find that God is looking to find his followers _____.

9. Paul states in 1 Corinthians 5:11 that believers should not spend excessive time with, or be influenced by, other believers who continue to purposefully be involved in sin.

    True   /or/   False

10. In 1 Corinthians 6:12, Paul says that even though something is not forbidden for us in the law, it may not be helpful to our spiritual walk because it can take hold and overpower us.

    True   /or/   False

11. Paul declares that, as Christians, we have been bought with a _____.

12. Knowledge makes one proud, but _____ builds each other up.

13. Never let your freedom in Christ become a stumbling block to those who are _____.

14. God is faithful, and will never allow you to be tempted beyond your ability to withstand. God will:

    A. also make a way of escape from the temptation, so that you can endure the test.
    B. make the temptation disappear just in the nick of time.
    C. make the temptations more difficult as time goes on.

15. In Romans 10:31, we are called to do everything to the glory of _____.

16. According to Romans 11:26, what does the Lord's Supper remind the believer of?

    A. Personal sin and shame
    B. A time of feast and endless eating
    C. The Lord's death and his eventual return

17. According to Romans 12:4-6, our various ministry gifts come from:

    A. our own talents that we have improved
    B. the one and only God above
    C. being taught in Bible study classes

18. What are some particular gifts of servanthood mentioned in Romans 12:28?

    (1) First, _____,

    (2) Second, _____,

    (3) Third, _____,

    (4) After that _____,

    (5) Then _____,

    (6) _____,

    (7) _____,

    (8) _____.

19. "And now abides faith, hope and love. The greatest of these is _____."

20. In Romans 14:22, Paul says that "tongues" (speaking in another known language) is a sign for unbelievers, but the clear proclamation of the gospel is to be preached and given to believers.

   True   /or/   False

21. God is not the author of confusion but of _____.

22. Let all things be done decently and _____.

23. Because of Adam we shall all die, but through Christ we can all be made _____.

24. The last enemy that shall be destroyed is _____.

2 CORINTHIANS

1. What word is repeated four times in this one verse, 2 Corinthians 1:4?

   A. comfort
   B. suffering
   C. evil

2. In its present and past tense, what verb is used five times in this one verse, 2 Corinthians 2:10?

   A. give
   B. send
   C. forgive

3. In 2 Corinthians 4:8-9, we may find troubles all around us but we never:

   A. cry.
   B. despair.
   C. take revenge.

4. We, as believers, walk by _____ and not by sight.

5. Who will stand before Christ and face judgment, according to 2 Corinthians 5:10?

   A. Everyone
   B. No one
   C. Only the hypocrites

6. We find in 2 Corinthians 5:18 that every believer is given the ministry of _____.

7. Paul confesses that he was given a "thorn in the flesh" to help him stay humble and not exalted.

     True   /or/   False

8. Paul prayed that God would remove the "thorn." God's answer was:

    A. "My grace is sufficient for you. My strength is made perfect in weakness."
    B. "Get over it."
    C. "Hang in there, and I'll get back to you."

1 CORINTHIANS, 2 CORINTHIANS. Write the main facts, ideas and your personal thoughts on these books::

1 CORINTHIANS:_____

_____

_____

2 CORINTHIANS:_____

_____

_____

Section 22 – GALATIANS and EPHESIANS

GALATIANS

PASSAGE	*THEME*
Galatians 1:6-16	There is no other Gospel but that of Christ
Galatians 2:16 – 3:29	Justification is not through the law but through faith in Jesus
Galatians 5:1-26	Living by faith and the fruit of the Spirit
Galatians 6:1-10	Applying faith to everyday life

VERSES TO REMEMBER:		
	Galatians 3:26-28	*Everyone is equal in Christ*
	Galatians 4:5	*We are adopted into God's family*
	Galatians 5:22-23	*The fruit of the Spirit*

EPHESIANS

PASSAGE	*THEME*
Ephesians 1:3-14	Believers are chosen, predestined, adopted, an inheritance
Ephesians 2:1-22	The reconciliation of sinners by grace and faith
Ephesians 3:1-21	Knowing the fullness of God's love and grace
Ephesians 4:1-32	The bond and unity of the Spirit
Ephesians 5:1 – 6:9	Holiness in everyday life, marriage and parenting
Ephesians 6:10-18	The whole armor of God

VERSES TO REMEMBER:		
	Ephesians 2:8-10	*We are God's workmanship*
	Ephesians 4:5	*One Lord, one faith, one baptism*
	Ephesians 4:32	*Be kind and forgiving*
	Ephesians 5:18	*Be filled with the Spirit*
	Ephesians 6:1	*Children, obey your parents*
	Ephesians 6:11	*Put on the whole armor of God*

Section 22 – REVIEW of GALATIANS and EPHESIANS

GALATIANS

1. Paul shares that, after his conversion, he went to Arabia and Damascus. Then he returned to Jerusalem after:

      a. 40 days
      b. 3 months
      c. 3 years

2. Arriving in Jerusalem, how many days did Paul spend with Peter?_____

3. In Galatians 2:11-16, Paul confronted Peter's hypocricy.

    True   /or/   False

4. In Galatians 3:28, we find that there are no distinctions or levels of Christians.

    True   /or/   False

5. In Galatians 5:19-23, Paul marks the contrast between life in the flesh and life in the Spirit. When the works of the flesh are manifested, there is sin. Name 9 sins from Paul's list:

    (1)_____

    (2)_____

    (3)_____

    (4)_____

    (5)_____

    (6)_____

    (7)_____

    (8)_____

    (9)_____

6. Now, name the fruit of the Spirit from Paul's list:

(1)_____

(2)_____

(3)_____

(4)_____

(5)_____

(6)_____

(7)_____

(8)_____

(9)_____

7. Paul writes: "Whatever a person sows, that will be what that person shall also _____."

EPHESIANS

1. Paul tells the saints (redeemed) in Ephesus that all believers have:

(1) redemption through the _____, and

(2) the forgiveness of _____, according to the riches of God's grace.

2. Paul mentions that he never ceases to give thanks for the believers in Ephesus, and that:

    A. he continues to make mention of them in his prayers.
    B. he wants to be thanked in return.
    C. he will be sending them a Hallmark card.

3. Paul says that we are saved by _____ through _____.

4. Paul, however, also says that we can find salvation through our earthly works.

    True   /or/   False

5. Ephesians 2:18 tells us that we have access by the Spirit to the Father through _____.

6. In Ephesians 6:19, Paul's prayer is that the faithful would know the _____ of Christ and be filled with all the fullness of God.

7. What word is used repeatedly (eight times) in Ephesians 4:4-7?

    A. "prisoner"
    B. "suffering"
    C. "one"

8. In Ephesians 4:11-12, we find that God gave apostles, prophets, evangelists, as well as pastors and teachers for:

    (1) the perfecting of the _____,

    (2) the work of the _____, and

    (3) the building up (edifying) of the _____.

9. As Christians, our attitude should cause us to be kind, tenderhearted and forgiving.

    True   /or/   False

10. Paul instructs wives to _____ to their husbands, as unto the Lord.

11. Paul tells husbands to love their wives even as Christ also loved _____.

12. Children are commanded to _____ their parents in the Lord.

13. "_____, do not provoke your children but bring them up in the nurture and teaching of the Lord."

14. Paul calls Christians to put on "the whole armor of God." In Ephesians 6:14-17, he lists:

    (1) the loins bound up and covered with _____,

    (2) the breastplate of _____,

    (3) feet with shod with the preparation of the _____,

    (4) the shield of _____,

    (5) the helmet of _____,

    (6) the sword of the _____.

GALATIANS, EPHESIANS. Write the main facts, ideas and your personal thoughts on these books:

GALATIANS:_____

_____

EPHESIANS:_____

_____

Section 23 – PHILIPPIANS and COLOSSIANS

PHILIPPIANS

PASSAGE

THEME

Philippians 1:11-26   All that happens to me brings glory to Christ
Philippians 1:27 – 2:18   Be humble and unified, separating yourselves from strife
Philippians 3:1 – 4:13   Rejoice, be confident and keep your focus on Christ

VERSES TO REMEMBER:

Philippians 1:21	*For to me to live is Christ, to die is gain*
Philippians 2:9-11	*The exaltation of Christ*
Philippians 3:14	*I press toward the mark for the prize*
Philippians 4:8-9	*Think on these things*
Philippians 4:13	*I can do all things through Christ*
Philippians 4:19	*But my God shall supply all your need*

COLOSSIANS

PASSAGE

THEME

Colossians 1:3-12   Overview of the redemptive life in Christ
Colossians 1:13-22   The redemptive work of Christ for reconciliation
Colossians 2:6 – 3:17   Living the everyday life as a Christian
Colossians 3:18-25   Commands for Christian living in marriage, parenting and the workplace

VERSES TO REMEMBER:

Colossians 1:18	*Jesus is the head of the Church*
Colossians 3:2	*Set your affections on things above*
Colossians 3:17,23	*The daily goal of the believer*

Section 23 – REVIEW of PHILIPPIANS and COLOSSIANS

PHILIPPIANS

1. Paul says, "For to me to live is Christ, and to die is _____."

2. Paul cautions the Philippian believers that nothing should be done through strife or personal glory.

     True   /or/   False

3. Christians should have the same mindset of Christ, namely to become as a:

    A. servant
    B. king
    C. priest

4. God has exalted Jesus and given him a name above every name, and that at the name of Jesus:

    A. every knee will bow and every tongue will confess that Jesus Christ is Lord.
    B. the proud in spirit will continue to defy God with no apparent final judgment.
    C. the unbelievers will be able to withstand the fury of God's wrath.

5. In Philippians 3:13-14, we are reminded that we have not fully achieved perfection in this life. We are to press on toward the mark for the prize of the

    _____ of God.

6. Paul's words of encouragement: "Rejoice...

    A. ...in the Lord always, and again I say rejoice."
    B. ...only in the good times."
    C. ...now because persecution is on the way."

7. When your heart is troubled, the peace of God, which surpasses all earthly understanding, will keep

    your _____

    and _____ through Christ Jesus.

8. Paul gives many things for Christians to consider and, if there be any virtue or praise, think on these things:

    (1) whatsoever things are _____,

    (2) whatsoever things are _____,

    (3) whatsoever things are _____,

    (4) whatsoever things are _____,

    (5) whatsoever things are _____,

    (6) whatsoever things are _____.

9. Paul complained that he had never learned to be content in whatever place or condition he was in.

    True   /or/   False

10. Paul expressed supreme confidence when he said "I can do all things through...

    A. ...my God-given talents and gifts."
    B. ...the assistance of all the saints around me."
    C. ...Christ, who continues to strengthen me."

11. Christians need not worry or fret because "...God shall supply every need according to...

    A. ...the sacrifices that are offered at the temple."
    B. ...his riches in glory in Christ Jesus."
    C. ...the financial ability of the saints around the world."

COLOSSIANS

1. In Colossians 1:14-17, who is being described?

    A. Jesus, the Son of God
    B. Paul, the Apostle
    C. Timothy, the brother in Christ

2. The head of the church is:

    _____.

3. In Colossians 2:6-7, those who have received Christ were encouraged to walk the lifestyle of Christ. As the new believers were taught, they were...

    A. rooted, built up and established in the faith.
    B. confused and bewildered.
    C. dysfunctional and crazy.

4. Paul asserted that the fullness of the Godhead was in Jesus.

    True   /or/   False

5. If we are followers of Christ, we must then set our affection and heart and mind on...

    A. things above rather than on the things of this earth.
    B. the day-to-day worries that God will take care of.
    C. nothing of consequence, because God will take care of everything.

6. In Colossians 3:5-10, Paul points out the things that should not be a part of the Christian life. Which of the following is NOT in Paul's list of the disobedient life?

    A. Love, joy, peace
    B. Fornication, evil desire, covetousness
    C. Malice, blasphemy, lying to one another

7. In Colossians 3:12-14, Paul then gives a list of virtues that the Christian should embrace. From this passage of Scripture, name three:

    (1)_____

    (2)_____

    (3)_____

8. "And whatever you do in word or deed, do all in the name of

    _____."

9. In Colossians 3:18-21, the focus of the Scriptures is marriage and family.

    True   /or/   False

PHILIPPIANS, COLOSSIANS. Write the main facts, ideas and your personal thoughts on these books:

PHILIPPIANS:_____

_____

_____

COLOSSIANS:_____

_____

_____

Section 24 – 1 THESSALONIANS and 2 THESSALONIANS

1 THESSALONIANS

PASSAGE   _THEME_

1 Thessalonians 1:2-10   Thanksgiving for the example and witness of the believers
1 Thessalonians 2:1-20   Believers' lives demonstrate that the Gospel has not gone out in vain
1 Thessalonians 3:1 – 4:12   Exhortation to holy living
1 Thessalonians 4:13 – 5:11   Be ready for the coming of the Lord
1 Thessalonians 5:12-24   Commands for living a godly life

    VERSES TO REMEMBER: _1 Thessalonians 4:7_   _God has called us to holiness_
                                        1 Thessalonians 4:16   _The second coming of Jesus_
                                        1 Thessalonians 5:22   _Abstain from the appearance of evil_

2 THESSALONIANS

PASSAGE   _THEME_

2 Thessalonians 1:3 – 2:17   Encouragement to stay faithful in persecution, being chosen by God
2 Thessalonians 3:11-15   Live the faithful life and admonish others in love

    VERSES TO REMEMBER: _2 Thessalonians 2:15_   _Stand fast in Biblical teachings_
                                        2 Thessalonians 3:13   _Be not weary in well doing_

Section 24 – REVIEW of 1 THESSALONIANS and 2 THESSALONIANS

1 THESSALONIANS

1. What three individuals with a missionary zeal are named in 1 Thessalonians 1:1?

    (1)_____

    (2)_____

    (3)_____

2. The Thessalonian believers had previously worshipped...

    A. idols
    B. Paul
    C. food

3. Why had Timothy been sent to the church in Thessalonica?

    A. To be a spy in the fellowship
    B. To both establish and comfort the believers in their faith
    C. To take up an offering to support Paul's ministry elsewhere

4. In 1 Thessalonians 4:7, Christians are called to...

    A. uncleanness
    B. fornication
    C. holiness

5. In 1 Thessalonians 4:11, Paul commanded the believers to...

    A. keep focus on their own business and stay busy with peace and self-control
    B. help others even when it destroys lives and reputations
    C. be lazy in order to save their energy for the work of evangelism

6. When Jesus returns, he shall descend from heaven...

    A. ...with a shout, with the voice of the archangel and with the trump of God.
    B. ...like a dove.
    C. ...in a flaming chariot.

7. When Jesus comes again, who shall rise first?

    A. Those in Israel
    B. The dead in Christ
    C. Those who have been baptized

8. The Christian attitude and lifestyle is found in 1 Thessalonians 5:11-22. Fill in the blanks:

verse 11 -   encourage yourselves and _____ one another

verse 12 -   get to know those who _____ among you

verse 13 -   give honor and esteem to others for their work and be at _____

verse 14 -   _____ the unruly,

                 _____ the feeble of mind,

                 _____ the weak,

                 _____ be _____ with everyone

verse 15 -   do not repay evil for _____

verse 16 -   _____ evermore

verse 17 -   _____ without ceasing

verse 18 -   in everything give _____

verse 19 -   do not _____ the Spirit

verse 20 -   do not despise _____

verse 21 -   _____ all things

verse 22 -   abstain from all appearance of _____

2 THESSALONIANS

1. When others cause us trouble, who will be our righteous vindicator and repay them with suffering?

    A. God   B. Our spouse   C. The judicial system

2. In 2 Thessalonians 3:3, how is God described?

    A. The Lord is deceptive in all ways
    B. The Lord is far away in the heavens
    C. The Lord is faithful

3. In 2 Thessalonians 3:8-10, Paul makes the case that those who do not work should not _____.

4. We as believers may get tired, but we are never to be weary in _____.

1 THESSALONIANS, 2 THESSALONIANS. Write the main facts, ideas and your personal thoughts on these books:

1 THESSALONIANS:_____

_____

_____

2 THESSALONIANS:_____

_____

_____

Section 25 – 1 TIMOTHY, 2 TIMOTHY, TITUS and PHILEMON

1 TIMOTHY

PASSAGE	*THEME*
1 Timothy 2:1-8	Exhortation to prayer
1 Timothy 2:9-15	Teachings concerning women in the church
1 Timothy 3:1-13	Qualifications of pastors and deacons
1 Timothy 4:6-16	How to grow up in Christ for the sake of ministry
1 Timothy 5:1-25	How to treat elders and widows
1 Timothy 6:1-21	Live the righteous life and avoid false teaching

VERSES TO REMEMBER:	*1 Timothy 4:12*	*A worthy example of Christian living*
	1 Timothy 6:10	*The love of money is the root of all evil*
	1 Timothy 6:11-12	*Pursue good and fight the good fight*

2 TIMOTHY

PASSAGE	*THEME*
2 Timothy 1:6 – 2:26	Be strong, be faithful and grow in the grace of Christ
2 Timothy 3:1-17	When apostasy and persecutions come, continue in Scripture study
2 Timothy 4:1-8	Preach the Word, proclaim the truth, keep the faith

VERSES TO REMEMBER:	*2 Timothy 2:3*	*Be a soldier for Christ*
	2 Timothy 2:15	*Study to be approved unto God*
	2 Timothy 3:16	*All Scripture is by inspiration of God*

TITUS

PASSAGE	*THEME*
Titus 1:5-9	Qualifications of elders and bishops
Titus 2:1-15	Exhortation to all ages and genders concerning righteous living
Titus 3:1-11	The attitudes necessary for the Christian life

VERSES TO REMEMBER:	*Titus 2:1*	*Speak things that are sound doctrine*
	Titus 3:9	*Things to avoid*

PHILEMON

<u>PASSAGE</u>   <u>THEME</u>

Philemon 8-21   Appeal to the church to receive a runaway slave as a brother in Christ

VERSE TO REMEMBER: *Philemon 17*   *Receive Onesimus as you would me*

Section 25 – REVIEW of 1 TIMOTHY, 2 TIMOTHY, TITUS and PHILEMON

1 TIMOTHY

1. Paul considered Timothy his _____ in the faith.

2. Paul points out that the law is good, and that it is for the disobedient rather than the righteous.

     True   /or/   False

3. According to 1 Timothy 1:15, what was Jesus' purpose on earth?

    A. To save sinners
    B. To do many miracles
    C. To overthrow the Roman oppression of Israel

4. How many ways to salvation and heaven are there? In 1 Timothy 2:5, Paul says...

    A. there are many roads to God.
    B. there are many gods who can give life.
    C. there is only one God – and only one mediator between God and men, that is Christ Jesus.

5. In 1 Timothy 3:1-7, what are the qualifications of the church's leadership (bishop, overseer, pastor)?

    verse 2 -   must be _____

                   the husband of _____

                    _____

                    of good _____

                    given to _____

                    ability to _____

    verse 3 -   not prone to _____

                    not a _____

                    not greedy of _____

                    but _____

not a _____

and not _____

verse 4-5 -   one who _____

having his children _____

verse 6 -   not a _____

verse 7 -   must have a good _____

6. In 1 Timothy 3:8-13, the qualifications of the deacons (church servants, assistants to leadership) are discussed. The list is quite similar to that of the overseer.

    True   /or/   False

7. In 1 Timothy 5:8, what description is given to a person that does not honorably provide for his own?

    A. One who has denied the faith and is worse than an unbeliever
    B. One who needs to find outlets for extra time and energy
    C. One who will be honored at the convention for the lazy

8. The best combination of reputation and attitude is found in 1 Timothy 6:6:

    A. Hard worker with pride
    B. Godliness with contentment
    C. Strong thinker with distrust

9. Which of the following is the Scriptural truth found in 1 Timothy?

    A. Money is evil.
    B. The love of money is evil.
    C. The love of money is the root of all evil.

10. Paul tells the believers the things to stay away from in 1 Timothy 6:4-5,9-10. Then, he gives a list of six things that Christians should pursue in their Christian walk. In 1 Timothy 6:11, they are:

    (1)_____

    (2)_____

    (3)_____

156

(4)_____

(5)_____

(6)_____

2 TIMOTHY

1. What were the names of Timothy's mother and grandmother?

    Grandmother's name:_____

    Mother's name:_____

2. "God has not given us the spirit of fear, but of...

    (1)_____,

    (2)_____, and

    (3)_____.

3. According to 2 Timothy 1:9, does God have a purpose in saving and calling individuals to faith?

    Yes   /or/   No

4. Match the following verses with the vocation listed:

    _____ (1) 2 Timothy 2:3   A. athlete

    _____ (2) 2 Timothy 2:5   B. farmer

    _____ (3) 2 Timothy 2:6   C. soldier

5. In 2 Timothy 2:15, Christians must be studious and diligent to be able to:

    A. know rightly how to share the truth of Scripture
    B. obtain higher degrees of education
    C. score high on the evangelism tests

6. What four things must the believer pursue to follow the Lord, as found in 2 Timothy 2:22?

(1)_____

(2)_____

(3)_____

(4)_____

7. Fill in the blanks, according to 2 Timothy 3:16:

"All scripture is given by _____,

and is profitable for _____,

for _____,

for _____,

for _____."

8. Paul wrote in 2 Timothy 4:7: "I have _____ a good fight,

I have _____ my course,

I have _____ the faith."

9. In 2 Timothy 4:8, what is the reward in heaven for the believer?_____

TITUS

1. Paul asked Titus to remain in:

    A. Crete
    B. Jerusalem
    C. Tarsus

2. In Titus 1:5-9, the qualifications of those in positions of church leadership (elders) are given. What qualification is listed at the end (verse 9)?

    A. Ability to coordinate massive fundraisers
    B. Steadfast in scripture to be able to expound sound doctrine and persuade opposition
    C. Educated in the areas of administration and counseling

3. Match the verses with the topics:

_____ (1) Titus 2:2   A. Proper attributes of faithful servants and workers

_____ (2) Titus 2:3   B. Proper attributes of young women of faith

_____ (3) Titus 2:4-5   C. Proper attributes of older men of faith

_____ (4) Titus 2:6-8   D. Proper attributes of young men of faith

_____ (5) Titus 2:9-10   E. Proper attributes of older women of faith

4. What things should believers avoid, according to Titus 3:9?

(1)_____

(2)_____

(3)_____

(4)_____

PHILEMON

1. Paul calls himself a _____ of Jesus Christ.

2. Match the following verses with the correct phrase:

_____ verse 1   A. fellow laborers (plural)

_____ verse 2   B. fellow prisoner

_____ verse 23   C. fellow soldier

_____ verse 24   D. fellow laborer (singular)

1 TIMOTHY, 2 TIMOTHY, TITUS, PHILEMON. Write the main facts, ideas and your personal thoughts:

1 TIMOTHY:_____

_____

159

2 TIMOTHY:_____

_____

TITUS:_____

_____

PHILEMON:_____

_____

DIVISION TEN
HEBREWS - REVELATION

Section 26 – HEBREWS and JAMES

HEBREWS

PASSAGE	*THEME*
Hebrews 2:1 – 3:19	The great work of Christ for our salvation
Hebrews 4:1-16	There is still work to be done for the Kingdom's sake
Hebrews 5:1-14	Christ, the High Priest, learned obedience through suffering
Hebrews 6:1-20	After repentance, we must go forward in Christ to perfection
Hebrews 7:21 – 10:39	Contrast between the old and new covenants
Hebrews 11:1-40	Definition and examples of faith
Hebrews 12:1 -13:17	Running the race and enduring until the end

VERSES TO REMEMBER:

Hebrews 4:12	*Word of God is alive and powerful*
Hebrews 4:16	*Come boldly to the throne of grace*
Hebrews 8:6	*Jesus is mediator of the new covenant*
Hebrews 11:1	*Definition of faith*
Hebrews 11:6	*Without faith, we cannot please God*
Hebrews 12:1-2	*Running the race, looking to Jesus*

JAMES

PASSAGE	*THEME*
James 1:2-16	Faithfulness to endure all temptations
James 1:17 – 2:25	Hearing and acting on the Word of God shows faith at work
James 3:1-12	The dangers of the tongue
James 3:13 – 5:6	Warnings about false wisdom, worldliness, pride and treasure
James 5:7-20	Helping a brother in Christ through affliction and sin

VERSES TO REMEMBER:

James 1:12	*Blessings from enduring temptations*
James 1:22	*Be doers of the word, not just hearers*
James 2:20	*Faith without works is dead*
James 4:7	*Submit to God, flee the devil*
James 4:17	*The sin of omission*
James 5:16	*Prayer of a righteous man described*

Section 26 – REVIEW of HEBREWS and JAMES

HEBREWS

1. At the end of the verse in Hebrews 2:10, we find that believers are perfected and matured through...

    A. suffering
    B. wealth
    C. friendships

2. In Hebrews 3:13, we are to exhort and encourage one another _____.

3. We find a description of Scripture in Hebrews 4:12. "The word of God is...

    (1)_____

    (2)_____, and

    (3)_____, and is a

    (4)_____.

4. As children of God, we can come _____ to the throne of God.

5. In Hebrews 6:4-6, what does the Bible say about being renewed again unto repentance?

    A. It is feasible
    B. It is possible
    C. It is impossible

6. What is faith? "Faith is...

    (1) the _____,

    (2) the _____."

7. By faith, Abraham...

    A. obeyed
    B. prepared an ark
    C. was imprisoned and tortured

8. To run the faithful race with patience and perseverance, Christians are to...

    A. look to other mature Christians
    B. look inward
    C. look to Jesus

9. In Hebrews 13:1, believers are reminded to welcome and minister to strangers because...

    A. some of those individuals that we do not recognize may be angels.
    B. some of those individuals that we help may come back and give us money.
    C. some of those individuals that we show kindness to might otherwise harm us.

JAMES

1. When we are being tested and fall into various trials and temptations, what should be our attitude?

    A. Joy
    B. Anger
    C. Frustration

2. If a person lacks wisdom, what should he do?

    A. Read the philosophical works of great men
    B. Memorize poetry
    C. Take time to ask of God

3. "Every good gift and every perfect gift is from _____."

4. In James 1:19, the believer is commanded to be...

    (1) quick to _____

    (2) slow to _____

    (3) slow to _____

5. Christians are not only to be hearers of the Word, but also _____ of the Word.

6. If a person can keep every part of the law except one tiny portion, that person is...

    A. guilty of breaking the entire law
    B. guilty of only the small portion
    C. innocent because the majority of the law was kept

7. James writes that faith without works is _____.

8. In James 3:1-12, there is a discussion about the tongue (speaking and talking) and its ability to:

    A. cause evil, defilement and offenses by the fire of sin
    B. bring unity and harmony only
    C. call down tornados, hurricanes, hailstorms and earthquakes

9. In the Old Testament, Solomon talked of wisdom. In James 3:17, we find the description of wisdom:

    (1) wisdom is first _____,

    (2) then _____,

    (3) _____,

    (4) easy to _____,

    (5) full of _____ and

    (6) _____,

    (7) without _____,

    (8) and without _____.

10. What keeps the believer from receiving the blessings and gifts from God? In James 4:3 we find:

    A. You ask and do not receive because you ask wrongly, desiring to fulfill your unholy desires.
    B. You ask and do not receive because you have not used your previous blessings wisely.
    C. You ask and do not receive because you are using the wrong prayer language.

11. If you submit yourself to God and resist the Devil...

    A. the Devil will try harder and harder to lure you into temptation.
    B. the Devil will flee from you.
    C. the Devil will hang around just a little longer to get more help from your friends.

12. In James 5:1-6, we find a warning to the...

    A. poor
    B. middle class
    C. rich

13. Match the following:

_____ (1) If you are afflicted, then...   A. call for the elders to anoint and pray

_____ (2) If you are joyous, then...   B. pray

_____ (3) If you are sick, then...   C. sing psalms

14. "The effectual fervent prayer of a righteous man avails much."

   True   /or/   False

HEBREWS, JAMES. Write the main facts, ideas and your personal thoughts on these books:

HEBREWS:_____

_____

_____

JAMES:_____

_____

_____

Section 27 – 1 PETER, 2 PETER, 1 JOHN, 2 JOHN and 3 JOHN

1 PETER

PASSAGE	*THEME*
1 Peter 1:3 – 2:3	Call to holy living
1 Peter 2:4-25	Live as Christ would, even to the point of suffering
1 Peter 3:1-12	Commands to husbands and wives
1 Peter 4:1-19	How to live and think as Christ
1 Peter 5:1-10	How to abide in the faith, whether as the older or the younger generation

VERSES TO REMEMBER:		
	1 Peter 1:16	*Be holy because God is holy*
	1 Peter 2:9-10	*You are a chosen generation*
	1 Peter 2:17	*Honor men, love the church, fear God*
	1 Peter 5:7	*Cast all your cares on God*

2 PETER

PASSAGE	*THEME*
2 Peter 1:2-21	Grow in grace by being grounded in the Word
2 Peter 2:1-22	Caution to false prophets and teachers
2 Peter 3:1-18	Living in the certainty of the Lord's coming

VERSES TO REMEMBER:		
	2 Peter 1:21	*Prophetic words only came from God*
	2 Peter 3:18	*Grow in grace, knowledge of Jesus*

1 JOHN

PASSAGE   *THEME*

1 John 1:1 – 2:17   The truth about Light and Love
1 John 2:18 – 3:8   Teachings about enemies of Christ and about sin
1 John 3:9 – 5:3   The new birth brings about love and a life that hates sin
1 John 5:4 -21   The life in Christ is a victorious life, also being confident of eternal life

> *VERSES TO REMEMBER:*   *1 John 1:6-7*   *Understanding fellowship with God*
> *1 John 2:3*   *How to keep God's commandments*
> *1 John 4:7*   *Love one another*
> *1 John 5:5*   *The victorious Christian defined*

2 JOHN

PASSAGE   *THEME*

2 John 4-11   The commandment of love

> *VERSE TO REMEMBER:*   *2 John 6*   *To love God is to follow his commands*

3 JOHN

PASSAGE   *THEME*

3 John 5-12   Contrasting doing well for the Lord as opposed to doing evil

> *VERSE TO REMEMBER:*   *3 John 11*   *He that does good is of God*

Section 27 – REVIEW of 1 PETER, 2 PETER, 1 JOHN, 2 JOHN and 3 JOHN

1 PETER

1. Peter wrote this epistle to all of the following EXCEPT:

    A. Pontus, Galatia, Cappadocia
    B. Asia and Bithynia
    C. Judea and Samaria

2. Peter's three commands to the believers in 1 Peter 1:13 are:

    A. Strengthen your mind, be clear-minded, and keep a confident hope to the end
    B. Run to the hills, hide and pray because the day of the Lord is near
    C. Fight back, get angry and take no prisoners when the enemy comes

3. In 1 Peter 2:9, there are some phrases that describe God's people. What are the first four phrases?

    "But you are a...   (1)_____

                          (2)_____

                          (3)_____

                          (4)_____

4. What are the four short commands found in 1 Peter 2:17?

    (1)_____

    (2)_____

    (3)_____

    (4)_____

5. The behavior and attitudes of both wives and husbands are discussed in 1 Peter 3.

    1 Peter 3:1-6 apply to: wives /or/   husbands

    1 Peter 3:7 applies to: wives /or/   husbands

6. The Christian must always be ready to...

      A. ...give an answer to every man that asks you for the hope that is in you.
      B. ...help the unbeliever look up scripture to find answers.
      C. ...bring the heathen to church to hear the answers about faith.

7. The elders (overseers, pastors) are to "feed the flock" willingly and never for financial reward.

      True   /or/   False

8. Peter says that Christians can take all their burdens, anxieties and worries to God because:

      A. God needs something to do with his spare time.
      B. God can put them in a box to deal with at a later time.
      C. God cares for his children.

2 PETER

1. This epistle was not written to a particular geographical location of believers. It is addressed to:

      A. Those who received the same precious faith through the righteousness of God and Jesus
      B. Those who have received the baptism of Paul
      C. Those who have received the confirmation of the Jerusalem church

2. In 2 Peter 1:5-10, the believers are called to be diligent in their salvation and calling by...

      (1) adding _____ to their faith,

      (2) adding _____ to their virtue,

      (3) adding _____ to knowledge,

      (4) adding _____ to temperance,

      (5) adding _____ to patience,

      (6) adding _____ to godliness, and

      (7) adding _____ to brotherly kindness.

3. Holy men of God spoke and prophesied as they were moved and inspired by the Holy Spirit.

      True   /or/   False

4. In 2 Peter 3:18, Christians are commanded NOT to do which of the following?

    A. Grow in grace
    B. Grow in the knowledge of their Lord and Savior Jesus Christ
    C. Grow in awareness and the activities of sin

1 JOHN

1. In 1 John 1:5, John describes God. He says that God is:

    A. Darkness
    B. Cloudiness
    C. Light

2. What happens if we confess our sins?

    A. God is faithful and just to forgive us our sins
    B. God will forgive only those sins that he wants to
    C. God will not accept our confessions

3. In 1 John 2:16, a person is "of the world and not the Father" if they embrace what three things?

    (1) The lust of _____

    (2) The lust of _____

        And...

    (3) The pride of _____

4. In 1 John 3:4-9, it is written that...

    A. those who are born of God do not involve themselves in sin as a usual practice
    B. those who are born of God continue to sin voluntarily
    C. those who are born of God desire to do sinful activities on weekends

5. A major message for Christians (1 John 4:11) is that they should _____ one another.

6. John tells believers in 1 John 4:18 to show love through action and truth, not just words and talk.

    True   /or/   False

7. In 1 John 4:7-12, the word "love" (or one of its forms) is used how many times?

    A. three times
    B. six times
    C. thirteen times

8. According to 1 John 5:5, who is the victorious individual?

    A. The one who believes in the power of positive thinking
    B. The one who has the most money and power
    C. The one who believes that Jesus is the Son of God

2 JOHN

1. In the first four verses of this short epistle, how many times is the word "truth" used?

    A. once
    B. twice
    C. five times

2. In verse 6, those who love God will...

    A. ...live a lifestyle that abides by God's commandments.
    B. ...transgress the doctrines of Christ.
    C. ...partake of the evildoers deeds.

3 JOHN

1. In the first three verses of this letter, how many times is the word "truth" used?

    A. none
    B. four
    C. twenty

2. Do not follow that which is evil, but follow that which is _____.

1 PETER, 2 PETER, 1 JOHN, 2 JOHN, 3 JOHN. Write the main facts, ideas and your personal thoughts on these books:

1 PETER:_____

2 PETER:_____

1.JOHN:_____

2 JOHN:_____

3 JOHN:_____

Section 28 – JUDE and REVELATION

JUDE

PASSAGE	*THEME*
Jude 3-23	Judgment of evil and exhortation to building faith and love

VERSE TO REMEMBER: *Jude 20-21*   *Build your faith, pray and love God*

REVELATION

PASSAGE	*THEME*
Revelation 1:4 – 3:22	Messages to the Seven Churches
Revelation 4:1-11	The vision of God's throne
Revelation 5:1 – 11:19	The book, the seals and the trumpets
Revelation 12:1 – 14:5	War in heaven, Michael, the beasts, and the Lamb
Revelation 14:6 – 18:24	The angels, the vials and the fall of Babylon
Revelation 19:1-21	The marriage supper of the Lamb
Revelation 20:1-10	Satan bound for 1,000 years
Revelation 20:11-15	The great white throne of judgment
Revelation 21:1 – 22:21	The new heaven and the new earth, the new Jerusalem

VERSES TO REMEMBER:

Revelation 1:8, 22:13	*I am the Alpha and the Omega*
Revelation 1:18	*I have the keys of hell and of death*
Revelation 3:20	*Behold, I stand at the door and knock*
Revelation 17:14	*We are called, chosen and faithful*
Revelation 22:17	*The Spirit and the Bride say "come"*

Section 28 – REVIEW of JUDE and REVELATION

JUDE

1. Jude, the author, is the brother of _____.

2. Because of heresies that creep into the church, Christians must therefore (Jude verse 3):

    A. earnestly contend for the faith
    B. allow for differences in theology and accept the teachings of others
    C. leave and start another fellowship

REVELATION

1. John wrote to the seven churches in Asia. Name their geographical locations:

    (1)_____

    (2)_____

    (3)_____

    (4)_____

    (5)_____

    (6)_____

    (7)_____

2. At the end of each message to a particular church, John writes:

    "He that has an ear, let him _____."

3. John saw the heavenly throne. How many seats were there around the throne?

    A. 2 – one for Jesus and one for the Holy Spirit
    B. 12 – for the twelve tribes of Israel
    C. 24 – for the twenty-four elders

4. Look at Revelation 5:11. Compute the math – what is 10,000 times 10,000?

    A. 100,000
    B. 1,000,000
    C. 100,000,000

5. In Revelation chapter 6, how many seals were opened?

    A. none
    B. 3
    C. 6

6. In Revelation 8:1, what happened when the seventh seal was opened?

    A. A tumultuous noise was made for one hour
    B. There was silence in heaven for half an hour
    C. No one knows what happened

7. Revelation 12:7-9 gives an historical account of the great battle in heaven between:

    A. Michael and his angels against the Devil and his angels
    B. The dead in Christ against the dead who were still unbelievers
    C. Fire and water

8. In Revelation 14:1, the Lamb stood on mount Zion.

    True   /or/   False

9. In Revelation 17:5, what is the description given to Babylon?

    A. The mother of harlots and abominations of the earth
    B. The cradle of civilization
    C. The hope for all mankind

10. In Revelation 17:14, was is made against the Lamb, but the Lamb is victorious. Those who are with the Lamb were described as:

    (1)_____

    (2)_____

    (3)_____

11. A white horse comes with a rider named Faithful and True (Revelation 19:11). This rider has another name, as found in a later verse (Revelation 19:13). What is that other name?

The rider was clothed with a garment dipped in blood and his name was _____.

12. John sees God's judgment in Revelation 19:20. The beast and false prophet were both...

    A. thrown alive into a lake of fire burning with brimstone
    B. hanged from two tall trees
    C. given a pardon because they repented

13. In Revelation 20:2-3, the Devil will be cast into a bottomless pit and bound for 3 ½ years.

    True   /or/   False

14. In Revelation 20:10, all of the following is true EXCEPT:

    A. The devil is cast into the lake of fire and brimstone
    B. The devil joins the beast and the false prophet and will be tormented for ever and ever
    C. The devil finds release from torment after 1,000 years

15. In the final judgment (Revelation 20:14-15), what three things are thrown into the lake of fire?

    (1) _____

    (2) _____

    (3) _____

16. In Revelation 21:1, John saw a new _____ and a new _____.

17. A small bit of information about heaven is revealed in Revelation 21:4. There shall be no more tears, and there shall not be any more:

    (1)_____

    (2)_____

    (3)_____

    (4)_____

18. There is no temple building in the new heaven because the Lord God Almighty and the Lamb are the temple in it.

    True   /or/   False

19. In Revelation 22:8-9, John fell down to worship the angel but was instructed to...

    A. worship all the other angels as well
    B. don't bother to worship anything because there is no heaven
    C. worship God

JUDE, REVELATION. Write the main facts, ideas and your personal thoughts on these books:

JUDE:_____

REVELATION:_____

_____

_____

Congratulations, you did it!

You read the whole Bible through!

You now have the right to say to someone,

"Don't Say You Can't."

ANSWER SECTION

GENESIS

1. (1:3) Day 1 – Light
   (1:6,8) Day 2 – Firmament/Heavens
   (1:9-11) Day 3 – Seas, Land, Vegetation
   (1:14,16) Day 4 – Sun, Moon, Heavenly bodies
   (1:20-21) Day 5 – Water, Animals, Fowl
   (1:24,27) Day 6 – Animal Life, Man
2. (2:9) Tree of Life,
        Tree of Knowledge of Good and Evil
3. (2:17) True
4. (3:4) True
5. (4:1-2) Cain and Abel
6. (5:27) 969 years old
7. (6:15) Length – 300 cubits = 450 feet
           Width – 50 cubits = 75 feet
           Height – 30 cubits = 45 feet
8. (7:6) 600 years old
9. (9:13) Rainbow
10. (12:1) False
11. (16:5) Ishmael
12. (21:3) Isaac
13. (21:5) 100 years old
14. (24:51) Rebekah
15. (25:24-26) Esau and Jacob
16. (29:23-25) Leah
17. (29:20,27) 14 years total
18. (29:32) Reuben (by Leah)
    (29:33) Simeon (by Leah)
    (29:34) Levi (by Leah)
    (29:35) Judah (by Leah)
    (30:6) Dan (by Bilhah)
    (30:8) Naphtali (by Bilhah)
    (30:11) Gad (by Zilpah)
    (30:13) Asher (by Zilpah)
    (30:18) Issachar (by Leah)
    (30:20) Zebulun (by Leah)
    (30:24) Joseph (by Rachel)
    (35:18) Benjamin (by Rachel)
19. (30:24, 35:18) Joseph and Benjamin
20. (32:28) D
21. (37:25) Ishmaelites
22. (40:9-12) A
    (40:16-18) B
    (41:25) D
23. (48:1) Manasseh and Ephraim

EXODUS

1. (2:1) Levi
2. (2:8-9) Moses' mother
3. (2:10) Pharaoh's daughter
4. (2:12) Killed an Egyptian
5. (3:2,4) Angel of the Lord / God
6. (3:11, 4:1, 4:10) B
7. (4:14-16) B
8. (7:20) Blood
   (8:6) Frogs
   (8:17) Lice
   (8:24) Flies
   (9:6) Death of Cattle
   (9:10) Boils on People and Animals
   (9:23) Thunder, Hail and Fire
   (10:13-14) Wind and Locusts
   (10:22) Darkness for 3 Days
   (12:29) Death of First-Born of Egyptians
9. (12:7) Blood
10. (13:21) Cloud by day and Fire by night
11. (14:21) c
12. (16:13-15) Bread and Quail
13. (20:3) No other gods
    (20:4-6) No images to be made for worship
    (20:7) Do not take name of Lord in vain
    (20:8-11) Keep the Sabbath holy
    (20:12) Honor father and mother
    (2013) Do not murder (kill)
    (20:14) Do not commit adultery
    (20:15) Do not steal
    (20:16) Do not lie (bear false witness)
    (20:17) Do not covet (lust of persons/property)
14. (25:10) Length – 2.5 cubits = 45 inches
            Width – 1.5 cubits = 27 inches
            Height – 1.5 cubits = 27 inches
15. (30:10) a
16. (31:13) sign of sanctification
    (31:14) holy
    (31:15) rest
17. (32:1) b

LEVITICUS

1. (4:6) b
2. (10:1-2) Nadab And Abihu
3. (16:8) A

LEVITICUS (continued)
4. (16:21) True
5. (18:20,29) A
6. (25:11) Every 50 years
6. (27:30-32) A

NUMBERS
1. (1:3) 20 years and up
   (1:3) war
2. (1:47) C
3. (6:3-6) C
4. (9:5) A
5. (14:6-8) Joshua and Caleb
6. (16:31-33) A
7. (20:7-12) True
8. (22:28) Balaam
9. (27:18-23) Joshua

DEUTERONOMY
1. (6:5) heart, soul and might
2. (31:6) A
3. (31:8) True
4. (32:48-52) False

JOSHUA
1. (2:1) Rahab
2. (3:4) D
3. (6:4) C
4. (7:24-26) A
5. (12:24) C
6. (24:15) A

JUDGES
1. (2:1) C
2. (3:9-10) True
3. (4:21) Jael
4. (6:37) C
5. (7:6-7) 300
6. (7:20) Pitcher /Lamp in left hand
       Trumpet in right hand
7. (13:5) C
8. (20:21) First – 22,000
   (20:25) Second – 18,000
   (20:35) Third – 25,000

RUTH
1. (1:4) Orpah and Ruth
2. (1:21-22) Bethlehem

RUTH (continued)
3. (4:13) Ruth
4. (4:22) B

1 SAMUEL
1. (1:14) B
2. (1:24-28) True
3. (2:21) A
4. (3:9) C
5. (7:12) Ebenezer
6. (8:5) C
7. (10:1,17,24) Mizpeh
8. (15:7-9) True
9. (16:4) Bethlehem
10. (16:13) David
11. (17:4) 6 cubits and a span = 9 ft. 9 in. tall
12. (18:27) Michal
13. (19:10) B
14. (20:16, 23:18) Jonathan
15. (24:7, 26:9) True

2 SAMUEL
1. (5:3-5) Hebron
2. (5:5) 40 years, 6 months
3. (9:1,3,6-7) Mephibosheth
4. (12:24) C
5. (12:7,9) Nathan
6. (18:14) Absalom

1 KINGS
1. (1:33) A
2. (3:9-14) C
3. (6:2) Length – 60 cubits = 90 feet
            Width – 20 cubits = 30 feet
            Height – 30 cubits = 45 feet
4. (12:1,21-23) Rehoboam (Judah)
                  Jeroboam (Israel)
5. (16:31) Jezebel
6. (17:4) Ravens
7. (17:16-23) False
8. (18:38) A
9. (19:8) Horeb, the mount of God
10, (19:19) A

2 KINGS
1. (2:11) B
2. (2:14) Jordan
3. (5:10) C

2 KINGS (continued)
4. (9:33-35) True
5. (25:1-7) A

1 CHRONICLES
1. (4:1,9) A
2. (13:9-10) Uzza
3. (21:18) True

2 CHRONICLES
1. (3:17) Jachin (right), Boaz (left)
2. (5:13-14) Cloud
3. (7:1) C
4. (7:14) humble themselves
    Pray
    Seek My face
    Turn from their wicked ways
5. (28:6) C
6. (30:1) Passsover

EZRA
1. (1:1) Cyrus
2. (2:19) a
3. (7:13) C

NEHEMIAH
1. (1:1) Shushan
2. (2:29) Sanballat, Tobiah, Geshem
3. (8:1) C

ESTHER
1. (1:12) Vashti
2. (2:17) Esther
3. (3:6) Mordecai
4. (6:11,7:9-10) False
5. (9:26) C

JOB
1. (1:12) True
2. (1:14-15) oxen and asses
    (1:16) sheep
    (1:17) camels
    (1:19) sons
3. (2:9) C
4. (6:14,8:4,19:1-2) B
5. (42:10) C

PSALMS
1. (1:2) law of the Lord

PSALMS (continued)
2. (14:1) the fool
3. (18:2) C
4. (37:7) patiently
5. (90:10) 70 (or 80 with strength)
6. (100:2) with gladness and singing
7. (150:1-6) C

PROVERBS
1. (1:7) knowledge
2. (2:6) the Lord
3. (3:12) the ones He loves
4. (6:16-19) proud look
    lying tongue
    hands that shed innocent blood
    heart that devises wicked things
    feet that quickly run to mischief (sin)
    false witness who speaks lies
    one who sows discord in brethren
5. (15:1) soft answer
6. (16:18) pride
7. (22:1) great riches
8. (31:30) praised

ECCLESIASTES
1. (1:2,14) a
2. (5:4-5) Pay it
3. (12:13) Fear God, keep His commandments
4. (12:14) God

SONG OF SOLOMON
1. (5:16) Friend

ISAIAH
1. (1:1) Uzziah, Jotham, Ahaz, Hezekiah
2. (6:8) C
3. (9:6-7) A
4. (18:1) Ethiopia
5. (33:22) A
6. (61:1) bind up the broken hearted
    proclaim liberty to the captives
    open the prison to those who are bound

JEREMIAH
1. (1:5) C
2. (7:23) C
3. (20:1-2) B
4. (32:27) hard
5. (38:7) B

JEREMIAH (continued)

6. (39:11-12) Babylon
7. (52:31) Jehoiachin

LAMENTATIONS

1. (3:25) A

EZEKIEL

1. (1:1) Chebar
2. (1:3) Priest
3. (11:19-20) A
4. (18:4) It shall die
5. (20:20) C
6. (33:7) Watchman
7. (37:1-5) B
8. (43:26) B

DANIEL

1. (1:7) Belteshazzar
2. (1:7) Hananiah = Shadrach (C)
        Mishael = Meshach (A)
        Azariah = Abednego (B)
3. (3:27) A
4. (5:25) A
5. (6:16) C
6. (10:1-7) Cyrus

HOSEA

1. (1:3) Gomer

2. (1:4) Jezreel
   (1:6) Loruhamah
   (1:9) Loammi
3. (11:7) Backslide
4. (14:4) Heal Israel's backsliding and
        Love them freely

JOEL

1. (1:14) True
2. (2:28) A

AMOS

1. (1:1) Tekoa
2. (2:6) True
3. (9:15) B

OBADIAH

1. (v17) Zion

JONAH

1. (1:2) Nineveh
2. (1:3) A
3. (1:12) A
4. (1:17) C
5. (3:5) False
6. (4:1) False

MICAH

1. (1:1) Jotham, Ahaz, Hezekiah
2. (4:1-3) True
3. (6:8) To do justly,
        To love mercy, and
        To walk humbly with your God

NAHUM

1. (1:2) A

HABAKKUK

1. (1:6) False
2. (2:4) Faith

ZEPHANIAH

1. (1:1) Josiah
2. (1:15) False

HAGGAI

1. (1:1) Darius
2. (1:4-9) True

ZECHARIAH

1. (1:1) Darius
2. (4:6) My Spirit
3. (8:3) Truth
4. (9:9) An ass (donkey)

MALACHI

1. (1:11) a
2. (3:6) a
3. (3:8-10) c

MATTHEW, Chapters 1-10

1. (1:2) Abraham
2. (1:20) A
3. (2:1) Bethlehem
4. (2:1) Herod
5. (2:11) Gold, Frankincense, Myrrh
6. (3:13) John the Baptist

7. (4:2) C
8. (4:18-22) Simon Peter
Andrew (Simon's brother)
James, son of Zebedee
John (James' brother)
9. (4:24) True
10. (5:3) Poor in spirit
(5:4) They that mourn
(5:5) Meek
(5:6) They which do hunger and thirst after righteousness
(5:7) Merciful
(5:8) Poor in heart
(5:9) Peacemakers
(5:10) They which are persecuted for righteousness' sake
11. (5:17) False
12. (6:12) True
13. (6:22) B
14. (7:21) A
15. (8:26) A
16. (9:7,22-33) C
17. (10:2-4) Simon Peter
Andrew
James, son of Zebedee
John
Philip
Bartholomew
Thomas
Matthew
James, son of Alpheus
Lebbeus Thaddeus
Simon the Canaanite
Judas Iscariot
18. (10:7) preach
(10:8) heal
(10:8) cleanse
(10:8) raise
(10:8) cast

MATTHEW, Chapters 11-28
1. (11:28) C
2. (12:8) Son of man (Jesus)
3. (12:13) B
4.(12:31) A
5. (13:34) C
6. (14:10) Beheaded
7. (14:17) A

8. (14:26,29) True
9. (16:14) John the Baptist
Elijah
Jeremiah
One of the prophets
10. (16:16) The Christ, the Son of the Living God
11. (17:2-9) C
12. (18:3) A
13. (19:22) B
14. (21:8-9) C
15. (22:21) False
16. (22:39) C
17. (24:6-31) C
18. (24:36) False
19. (26:3) C
20. (26:25,47-49) Judas
21. (26:36) Gethsemane
22. (26:56) False
23. (26:65) B
24. (27:2) A
25. (27:5) A
26. (27:17) Barabbas
27. (27:24) Innocent
28. (27:28-48) c
29. (27:45) 3 hours
30. (27:54) A
31. (27:57) B
32. (28:1-5) C
33. (28:6) A
34. (28:7) A
35. (28:19) C

MARK
1. (1:4-6) A
2. (1:5) B
3. (1:17) C
4. (1:16) A
5. (1:19-20) A
6. (1:23-27) C
7. (1:30-31) B
8. (2:15) A
9. (3:5) True
10. (3:15) Preach
Power to heal sicknesses
Cast out devils
11. (3:35) C
12. (5:19) A
13. (6:1-6) A

MARK (continued)
14. (6:17) B
15. (6:43) 12
16. (7:18-23) Outward
17. (7:36) C
18. (8:12) B
19. (9:29) A
20. (9:34) C
21. (10:2-9) A
22. (10:41) C
23. (10:52) A
24. (11:17) B
25. (12:37) A
26. (12:44) A
27. (14:3) Head
28. (14:22) Body
29. (14:31) B
30. (14:33) Peter, James, John
31. (14:72) Wept
32. (15:22) Golgotha
33. (15:38) A
34. (16:11) False
35. (16:19) True

LUKE
1. (1:1) Theophilus
2. (1:13) John
3. (1:19) Gabriel
4. (1:27) Mary
5. (1:41) True
6. (1:63) A
7. (2:4) Bethlehem
8. (2:8-10) C
9. (2:22) Jerusalem
10. (2:25-32) True
11. (2:45-46) A
12. (3:1) Herod (in Galilee)
        Philip (Herod's brother)
        Lysanias
13. (3:21-22) C
14. (3:38) Adam
15. (4:2) Nothing
16. (4:14-15) Synagogues
17. (4:28-29) A
18. (5:10-11) True
19. (5:32) Sinners
20. (6:12) B
21. (6:37) A

LUKE (continued)
22. (7:39) A
23. (8:2) B
24. (8:25) C
25. (8:51) A
26. (9:23) deny, cross, follow
27. (10:1) 70
28. (10:31-33) B
29. (11:9) C
30. (12:31) True
31. (13:14) True
32. (14:27) your cross, after me (Jesus)
33. (15:4,8,13) Sheep, Con, Son
34. (17:4)   (1)
35. (17:5) Increase our faith
36. (19:8) A
37. (19:40) A
38. (20:35) True
39. (22:8) B
40. (22:43) C
41. (22:54,66;23:1) C
42. (23:19) A
43. (23:36) Vinegar
44. (23:53) New
45. (24:18) B
46. (24:42) A

JOHN
1. (1:7) B
2. (1:14) Flesh
3. (1:17) C
4. (1:40-41) Simon
5. (2:1) Cana
6. (3:16) A
7. (4:1) True
8. (4:2) A
9. (4:24) C
10. (5:5) A
11. (5:27) Execute judgment
12. (6:15) King
13. (6:35) Bread
14. (8:7) A
15. (8:58) I AM!
16. (9:34) C
17. (10:30) One
18. (11:35) Jesus wept
19. (11:43) B
20. (11:50-51) False

JOHN (continued)
21. (12:20) A
22. (13:2,27) Devil / Satan
23. (13:5) B
24. (13:35) A
25. (14:3) B
26. (14:15) Commandments
27. (15:14) Friends
28. (16:7) Comforter
29. (17:20) A
30. (18:10) C
31. (18:38) C
32. (18:38) A
33. (19:19) A
34. (19:30) A
35. (19:34) C
36. (20:3-6) B
37. (20:12) 2
38. (20:15) B
39. (20:25) A
40. (21:11) 153
41. (21:17) C

ACTS, Chapters 1-9
1. (1:1) A
2. (1:8)   (1)Jerusalem
            (2)Judea
            (3)Samaria
            (4)Uttermost part of the earth
3. (1:23) (1)Joseph Barsabas Justus
            (2)Matthias
4. (1:26) Matthias
5. (2:8-11) B
6. (2:14) A
7. (2:41) 3,000 conversions
8. (2:44-45) C
9. (3:6) C
10. (4:10-12) A
11. (4:31) A
12. (4:32-35) A
13. (5:5,10) A
14. (5:18) True
15. (5:19-20) C
16. (5:21) B
17. (5:29) Man
18. (5:34-40) B

ACTS, Chapters 1-9 (continued)
19. (6:5) Stephen
            Philip
            Prochorus
            Nicanor
            Timon
            Parmenas
            Nicolas
20. (7:59-60) Stephen
21. (8:1) A
22. (8:27) A
23. (8:37) B
24. (9:2-3) C
25. (9:9) B
26. (9:13-14) A
27. (9:15) B
28. (9:30) A
29. (9:40-41) True

ACTS, Chapters 10-28
1. (10:1) B
2. (10:9-16) A
3. (10:44-46) A
4. (11:1-2) False
5. (11:26) A
6. (12:3-5) Peter
7. (12:6) 2
8. (12:7-11) B
9. (12:13-14) A
10. (13:2-3) A
11. (13:9) B
12. (13:44) A
13. (15:5) C
14. (15:23-28) True
15. (15:29) A
16. (16:12) Philippi
17. (16:27-29) A
18. (17:6-7) Jason
19. (17:22) Mars Hill
20. (18:1) Corinth
21. (19:5) C
22. (20:2-3) Greece
23. (20:36) B
24. (21:37-22:16) A
25. (23:8) A
26. (23:24) Felix
27. (24:27) Porcius Festus
28. (26:28) C

ACTS, Chapters 10-28 (continued)
29. (26:31-32) True
30. (28:1) Melita
31. (28:6) B
32. (28:24) B

ROMANS
1. (1:1) Paul, a servant of Jesus Christ
2. (1:16) False
3. (1:26) Vile affections
   (1:27) Men lying with men (homosexuality)
   (1:28) Reprobate mind
   (1:29) Unrighteousness
        Fornication
        Wickedness
        Covetousness
        Maliciousness
        Envy
        Murder
        Debate (strife)
        Deceit
        Malignity (evil motives)
        Whisperers (gossip)
   (1:30) Backbiters
        Haters of God
        Despiteful (insolent)
        Proud
        Boasters
        Inventors of evil things
        Disobedient to parents
   (1:31) Without understanding
        Covenant-breakers
        Without natural affection (heartless)
        Implacable (out of control)
        Unmerciful
4. (3:23) A
5. (5:1) B
6. (5:8) Yes
7. (6:1-12) No
8. (6:23) C
9. (7:22-23) A
10. (8:15) Adoption
11. (8:38) Death
        Life
        Angels
        Principalities
        Powers
        Things present
        Things to come

ROMANS (continued)
11.(continued) (8:39) Height
        Depth
        Any other creature
12. (10:9) Mouth
        Heart
13. (10:13) A
14. (10:17) C
15. (12:1) Living sacrifice
16. (12:2) A
17. (12:10) False
18. (12:14) True
19. (13:10) Love
20. (16:17) C

1 CORINTHIANS
1. (1:1) Apostle
2. (1:3) True
3. (1:9) Faithful
4. (1:18) A
5. (2:16) C
6. (3:9) True
7. (3:16) Temple
8. (4:2) Faithful
9. (5:11) True
10. (6:12) True
11. (6:20;7:23) Price
12. (8:1) Charity (Love)
13. (8:9) Weak
14. (10:13) A
15. (10:31) God
16. (11:26) C
17. (12:4-6) B
18. (12:28) Apostles
        Prophets
        Teachers
        Miracles
        Healings
        Helps
        Governments
        Diversity of tongues (languages)
19. (13:13) Charity (Love)
20. (14:22) True
21. (14:33) Peace
22. (14:40) In order
23. (15:22) Alive
24. (15:26) Death

2 CORINTHIANS
1. (1:4) A
2. (2:10) C
3. (4:8-9) B
4. (5:7) Faith
5. (5:10) A
6. (5:18) Reconciliation
7. (12:7) True
8. (12:9) A

GALATIANS
1. (1:17-18) c
2. (1:18) 15 days
3. (2:11-16) True
4. (3:28) True
5. (5:19) Adultery
  Fornication
  Uncleanness
  Lasciviousness
  (5:20) Idolatry
  Witchcraft
  Hatred
  Variance (unstable)
  Emulations (jealousies)
  Wrath
  Strife
  Seditions (divisions)
  Heresies
  (5:21) Envyings
  Murders
  Drunkenness
  Revelings
6. (5:22) Love
  Joy
  Peace
  Long-suffering
  Gentleness
  Faith
  (5:23) Meekness
  Temperance
7. (6:7) Reap

EPHESIANS
1. (1:7) His (Jesus') blood
  Sin
2. (1:16) A
3. (2:8) Grace through faith
4. (2:9) False
5. (2:12-18) Him (Jesus)

PHILIPPIANS
1. (1:1) Gain
2. (2:2-4) True
3. (2:5-7) A
4. (2:9-11) A
5. (3:13-14) High calling
6. (4:4) A
7. (4:7) Hearts, Minds
8. (4:8) True
  Honest
  Just
  Pure
  Lovely
  Good report
9. (4:11-12) False
10. (4:13) C
11. (4:19) B

COLOSSIANS
1. (1:3-4,14-17) A
2. (1:4,18) Jesus
3. (2:6-7) A
4. (2:6,9) True
5. (3:2) A
6. (3:5-10) A
7. (3:12) Bowels of mercies
  Kindness
  Humbleness of mind
  Meekness
  Long-suffering
  (3:13) Forbearing one another
  Forgiving one another
  (3:14) Charity (Love)
  (3:15) Peace of God
8. (3:17) The Lord Jesus
9. (3:18-21) True

1 THESSALONIANS
1. (1:1) Paul, Silvanus, Timothy
2. (1:9) A
3. (3:2) B
4. (4:7) C
5. (4:11) A
6. (4:16) A
7. (4:16) B
8. (5:11) Edify (build up)
  (5:12) Labor
  (5:13) Peace among yourselves
  (5:14) Warn, Comfort, Support, Be patient

1 THESSALONIANS (continued)

8. (5:11) Edify (build up)
   (5:12) Labor
   (5:13) Build peace among yourselves
   (5:14) Warn, Comfort, Support, Be patient
   (5:15) Evil
   (5:16) Rejoice
   (5:17) Pray
   (5:18) Thanks
   (5:19) Quench
   (5:20) Prophesyings (proclamation of Word of God)
   (5:21) Prove
   (5:22) Evil

2 THESSALONIANS

1. (1:6) A
2. (3:3) C
3. (3:8-10) Eat
4. (3:13) Well doing

1 TIMOTHY

1. (1:2) Son
2. (1:8-9) True
3. (1:15) A
4. (2:5) C
5. (3:2) Blameless
      One wife
      Vigilant
      Sober
      Good behavior
      Hospitality
      Teach
   (3:3) Drinking wine
      Striker (fighter)
      Filthy lucre (money)
      Patient
      Brawler
      Covetous
   (3:4) Rules his own house well
      Children in subjection
   (3:6) Novice (immature believer)
   (3:7) Report (reputation
6. (3:8-13) True
7. (5:8) A
8. (6:6) B
9. (6:10) C
10. (6:11) Righteousness, Godliness, Faith,
       Love, Patience, Meekness

2 TIMOTHY

1. (1:5) Grandmother Lois, Mother Eunice
2. (1:7) Power, Love, Sound mind
3. (1:9) Yes
4. (2:3) C
   (2:5) A
   (2:6) B
5. (2:15) A
6. (2:22) Righteousness, Faith, Love, Peace
7. (3:16) Inspiration of God
         Doctrine, Reproof, Correction, Instruction
8. (4:7) Fought, Finished, Kept
9. (4:8) Crown of righteousness

TITUS

1. (1:5) A
2. (1:9) B
3. (2:2) C
   (2:3) E
   (2:4-5) B
   (2:6-8) D
   (2:9-10) A
4. (3:9) Foolish questions
      Genealogies
      Contentions
      Strivings about the Law

PHILEMON

1. (v1) Prisoner
2. (v1) D
   (v2) C
   (v23) B
   (v24) A

HEBREWS

1. (2:10) A
2. (3:13) Daily
3. (4:12) Quick (alive and living)
      Powerful
      Sharper than any two-edged sword
      Discerner of thoughts, intents of heart
4. (4:16) Boldlly
5. (6:4-6) C
6. (11:1) Substance of things hoped for
      Substance of things not seen
7. (11:8) A
8. (12:2) C
9. (13:1) A

JAMES

1. (1:2) A
2. (1:5) C
3. (1:17) above, from the Father of Lights
4. (1:19) hear (listen)
   slow to speak
   slow to wrath
5. (1:22) Doers
6. (2:10) A
7. (2:17) Dead
8. (3:5-6) A
9. (3:17) Pure, Peaceable, Gentle, Be entreated, Mercy,
   Good fruits, Partiality, Hypocricy
10. (4:3) A
11. (4:7) B
12. (5:1) C
13. (5:13) afflicted – B
   joyous – C
   (5:14) sick – A
14. (5:16) True

1 PETER

1. (1:1) C
2. (1:14) A
3. (2:9) Chosen generation
   Royal priesthood
   Holy nation
   Peculiar (unique) people
4. (2:17) Honor all men
   Love the brotherhood
   Fear God
   Honor the King
5. (3:1-6) Wives
   (3:7) Husbands
6. (3:15) A
7. (5:2) True
8. (5:7) C

2 PETER

1. (1:1) A
2. (1:5) virtue to faith
   (1:5) knowledge to virtue
   (1:6) temperance to knowledge
   (1:6) patience to temperance
   (1:6) godliness to patience
   (1:7) brotherly kindness to godliness
   (1:8) charity (love) to brotherly kindness
3. (1:21) True
4. (3:18) C

1 JOHN

1. (1:5) C
2. (1:9) A
3. (2:16) the flesh, the eyes, life
4. (3:9) A
5. (3:11) Love
6. (3:18) True
7. (4:7-12) C
8. (5:5) C

2 JOHN

1. (v1-4) C
2. (v6) A

3 JOHN

1. (v1-4) B
2. (v11) good

JUDE

1. (v1) James
2. (v3) A

REVELATION

1. (2:1) Ephesus
   (2:8) Smyrna
   (2:12) Pergamos
   (2:18) Thyatira
   (3:1) Sardis
   (3:7) Philadelphia
   (3:14) Laodicea
2. (3:22) hear what the Spirit says to the churches
3. (4:4) C
4. (5:11) C
5. (6:12) C
6. (8:1) B
7. (12:7-9) A
8. (14:1) True
9. (17:5) A
10. (17:14) called, chosen, faithful
11. (19:13) The Word of God
12. (19:20) A
13. (20:2-3) False
14. (20:10) C
15. (20:14-15) Death and Hell and
   Those names not in Book of Life
16. (21:1) heaven, earth
17. (21:4) death, sorrow, crying, pain
18. (21:22) True
19. (22:8-9) C

ARE YOU A CHRISTIAN?

If you have completed this workbook, you have learned a great deal about God's plan for his creation. God has a plan for you!

The word *choice* is important here. Have you made a choice about what you will do with Jesus? Will you accept God's great love for your life? Can you trust the Scriptures and the testimony of others? Is it important enough or a high enough priority to get this settled for all of eternity? If you are a believer in Jesus Christ as Lord and Savior, this is just a refresher.

If you are not a believer, please read the following Scriptures carefully.

"For all have sinned and fall short of the glory of God."   Romans 3:23 (NASB)

EVERYONE HAS SINNED.

This is true. Everyone has made mistakes. No one is perfect. You have made serious errors in life, you have wronged someone, and you have faults. You are a sinner and, because of your imperfections, you are not able to obey all of God's commands and purposes in your own strength.

"For the wages of sin is death."   Romans 6:23 (NASB)

EVERYONE WILL DIE.

This is true. Every single person will die. No one lives forever. We are mere mortal human beings whose bodies will someday be lowered into a grave or ashes placed in a crypt. Our hearts will stop beating, and our breath will be no more. That means that we, you and I, will die sometime in the future.

"It is appointed for men to die once, and after this comes judgment." Hebrews 9:27 (NASB)

EVERYONE WILL FACE JUDGMENT.

This is true. After death and at God's appointed hour, we will all face judgment. We will be held accountable for all things thought, said and done. Every motive and every intention will be examined by an awesome and holy God. Because of our sinful nature and God's hatred of sin, we deserve an eternity apart from his love. Without right relationship with God, we face an eternity in hell.

EVERYONE CAN HAVE ETERNAL LIFE.

"For God so loved the world, that he gave his only begotten Son, that whoever believes in him should not perish but have eternal life."   John 3:16 (NASB)

This is true. God's love has provided a way of salvation and deliverance for all mankind from the penalty of sin. The curse and punishment for sin is eternal death, total separation from his blessed presence. However, God allowed his Son, Jesus, to die and pay the full price for our sins. The key to eternal life is faith, believing and receiving Jesus Christ as Lord and Savior.

"For by grace you have been saved through faith, and that not of yourselves. It is the gift of God; not as a result of works, that no one should boast." Ephesians 2:8-9 (NASB)

NO ONE CAN WORK FOR SALVATION.

This is true. God's gift of eternal life cannot be paid for or earned by works. It is completely free of cost, in the material and earthly sense. It is God's wonderful grace, his undeserved kindness, that provides an eternity with him. However, it is by our faith, our complete trust and abandonment to his ways and purposes, that he allows us to be his children. We become heirs to the kingdom of heaven.

"For whoever will call upon the name of the Lord will be saved." Romans 10:9 (NASB)

NO ONE CAN TAKE YOUR SALVATION AWAY.

This is true. God does not lie. This is God's guarantee and promise. We are assured of eternal life if we place our hope in the Lord. God's guarantee is sure and solid. Nobody can break God's grip on our hearts and lives for his kingdom's sake. We have a heavenly home that is secure.

*****

Where do you stand? What is your relationship with God? There is the old question that has been asked so many times, "If you died today and had to stand before God, and he asks you why should he let you into heaven, what would you say?"

We can't say, "Well, I went to church every Sunday."

It won't do any good to respond, "My parents were Christians!"

It's not enough to make the claim, "But I was a good person."

It won't be sufficient to assert that you helped the poor and gave to charities.

Here is the question:

Has there been a time when you allowed Jesus to be your friend, your Savior, your Lord?

Do you believe that Jesus…

…was the Christ,

…the very Son of God,

…who lived a perfect life,

…died an agonizing death on the cross for our sins,

…was buried in the grave,

…paid the price for the sins of mankind,

…and then was raised again to life

…by the Heavenly Father.

If you have given God full control and reign in your life through his Son, you can be confident in your eternity. If you have not let God have full authority and rule for your every decision in life, I urge you to do it now. It is not too late. In fact, the present moment is always the right time to give God your heart. Pray something like this: *"Dear God, I don't know everything about sin and death and eternity, but I do know that I am a sinner. Right now, I trust Jesus. Take my sins away and make me a new person. I want to live for you with all my heart. I know you will do it! Amen."*

If you have done that, you are a brand new child of God!

As a child of God, now you can go out and find a church to belong to. Don't be an orphan Christian! Find a place to grow and learn more of his love. Because, in God's love and comfort, we find peace. And that's why we started this workbook in the first place – to find a way to learn more about God and his great plan for the ages.

ABOUT THE AUTHOR

K. Galen Greenwalt is a pastor, author and counselor. He has been in the pastorate for over forty years.

He is a graduate of California Baptist University (B.A., B.S.) and Golden Gate Baptist Theological Seminary (M.Div., M.R.E.). He has also taken doctoral courses at the University of San Diego (Ed.D. in Leadership).

Pastor Galen has been involved in two new church starts – one in Hercules, California, and the other in Riverside, California. In addition, he has served in ministry and pastoral positions in several California churches (Rialto, Bakersfield, Rodeo, 29 Palms, and San Diego). He continues to pastor at The Vision Plus Church in Riverside. Pastor Galen has made many mission trips abroad and has done extensive travel. His mission trips include the Philippines, Russia, Bangladesh, India, Hong Kong and Japan. He has also served in volunteer chaplaincy positions (local police department, hospital and manufacturing corporation).

Galen has been a bi-vocational pastor for most of his ministry years – working for Kaiser Steel, Bechtel Petroleum, Coronado Stone, US Census Bureau; in addition to teaching college courses, middle school Special Education and working as an Education Coordinator for a non-public school system for Special Ed students.

This author is a military veteran of the Vietnam Era, serving in the Army as an infantry paratrooper at Ft. Benning, Georgia, and Bad Kreuznach , Germany (HQ 8th Infantry Division).

Galen has been married 39 years to his wife, Sondra. They have three children and four grandchildren at this time. As this goes to press, a fifth grandchild will soon join the Greenwalt clan.

ORDERING COPIES OF THIS BOOK:

This book is available for discount pricing in bulk orders.
Special discounts are also available for churches and non-profit organizations.

Please write the author:

revgalen@aol.com

Made in the USA
Charleston, SC
02 August 2011